HiSET Math

workbook

Activities, Exercises, and Two

Complete HiSET Mathematics

Practice Tests

By

Michael Smith & Reza Nazari

HiSET Math Workbook

Published in the United State of America By

The Math Notion

Email: info@Mathnotion.com

Web: www.MathNotion.com

About the Author

Michael Smith has been a math instructor for over a decade now. He holds a master's degree in Management. Since 2006, Michael has devoted his time to both teaching and developing exceptional math learning materials. As a Math instructor and test prep expert, Michael has worked with thousands of students. He has used the feedback of his students to develop a unique study program that can be used by students to drastically improve their math score fast and effectively.

- **HiSET Math Workbook**
- **TASC Math Workbook**
- **ASVAB Math Workbook**
- **AFOQT Math Workbook**
- **many Math Education Workbooks**
- **and some Mathematics books ...**

As an experienced Math teacher, Mr. Smith employs a variety of formats to help students achieve their goals: He tutors online and in person, he teaches students in large groups, and he provides training materials and textbooks through his website and through Amazon.

You can contact Michael via email at:

info@Mathnotion.com

HiSET Math Workbook

HiSET Math Workbook reviews all HiSET Math topics and provides students with the confidence and math skills they need to succeed on the HiSET Math. It is designed to address the needs of HiSET test takers who must have a working knowledge of basic Mathematics.

This comprehensive workbook with over 2,500 sample questions and 2 complete HiSET tests can help you fully prepare for the HiSET Math test. It provides you with an in-depth focus on the math portion of the exam, helping you master the math skills that students find the most troublesome. This is an incredibly useful tool for those who want to review all topics being covered on the HiSET Math test.

HiSET Math Workbook contains many exciting features to help you prepare for the HiSET Math test, including:

- Content 100% aligned with the 2019-2020 HiSET test
- Provided and tested by HiSET Math test experts
- Dynamic design and easy-to-follow activities
- A fun, interactive and concrete learning process
- Targeted, skill-building practices
- Complete coverage of all HiSET Math topics which you will be tested
- 2 full-length practice tests (featuring new question types) with detailed answers.

The only prep book you will ever need to ace the HiSET Math Test!

WWW.MathNotion.COM

… So Much More Online!

✓ FREE Math Lessons

✓ More Math Learning Books!

✓ Mathematics Worksheets

✓ Online Math Tutors

For a PDF Version of This Book

Please Visit WWW.MathNotion.com

Contents

Chapter 1: Whole Numbers, Real Numbers and Integers

Topics that you'll learn in this chapter:

- ➤ Rounding and Estimates

- ➤ Addition, Subtraction, Multiplication and Division Whole Number and Integers

- ➤ Arrange and ordering Integers and Numbers

- ➤ Comparing Integers, Order of Operations

- ➤ Mixed Integer Computations

- ➤ Integers and Absolute Value

"If people do not believe that mathematics is simple, it is only because they do not realize how complicated life is." — John von Neumann

Rounding and Estimates

✏️ Round each number to the underlined place value.

1) <u>8</u>8

2) <u>8</u>.15

3) <u>4</u>,315

4) 5<u>6</u>5

5) 1.<u>3</u>31

6) 1<u>8</u>.175

7) <u>2</u>.429

8) <u>3</u>85

9) 14.<u>2</u>3

10) 2,<u>9</u>97

11) 4.3<u>1</u>3

12) <u>7</u>.38

✏️ Estimate the sum by rounding each added to the nearest ten.

1) 17 + 18

2) 11 + 55

3) 203 + 56

4) 57 + 38

5) 213 + 74

6) 94 + 81

7) 19 + 167

8) 55 + 33

9) 96 + 49

10) 99 + 324

11) 823 + 488

12) 466 + 276

13) 5112 + 5792

14) 1245 + 2459

15) 5265 + 382

Whole Number Addition and Subtraction

✍ Solve.

1) Erika has just started her first job after graduating from college. Her yearly income is $30,000 per year. Erika's father income is $47,000 per year and her mother's income is $40,000. What is yearly income of Erika and her parents altogether?

2) A school had 708 students last year. If all last year students and 218 new students have registered for this year, how many students will there be in total?

3) Daniel has 820 marbles, Ethan has 500 marbles, and Emily has 340 marbles less than Daniel. How many marbles do they have in all?

4) Lisa had $856 dollars in her saving account. She gave $295 dollars to her brother, Tom. How much money does she have left?

✍ Find the missing number.

5) $540 - \text{.............} = 100$

6) $800 - \text{.............} = 220$

7) $\text{.............} - 2650 = 6700$

8) $85000 - 42000 = \text{.........}$

Whole Number Multiplication and Division

✏ **Multiply and divide.**

1) $120 \times 6 =$

2) $160 \times 30 =$

3) $600 \times 30 =$

4) $420 \times 20 =$

5) $250 \times 40 =$

6) $600 \times 40 =$

7) $215 \times 70 =$

8) $2000 \div 80 =$

9) $225 \div 25 =$

10) $315 \div 15 =$

11) $384 \div 12 =$

12) $740 \div 4 =$

13) $1925 \div 7 =$

14) $494 \div 13 =$

15) Alice and her two brothers have 7 boxes of crayons. Each box contains 66 crayons. How many crayons do Alice and her two brothers have?

16) A group of 125 students has collected $7236 for charity during last month. They decided to split the money evenly among 6 charities. How much will each charity receive?

Adding and Subtracting Integers

✏️ **Find the sum.**

1) $(-12) + (-3)$

2) $8 + (-11)$

3) $(-13) + 25$

4) $(-7) + 37$

5) $55 + (-15)$

6) $(-13) + (-4) + 5$

7) $2 + (-11) + (-30) + (9)$

8) $(-25) + (-11) + 36 + 9$

9) $(-5) + (-10) + (7 - 19)$

10) $3 + (-15) + (28 - 10)$

11) $(+35) + (+15) + (-20)$

12) $24 + 16 + (-13)$

✏️ **Find the difference.**

13) $(-3) - (-2\,3)$

14) $(-12) - (33)$

15) $(38) - (-12)$

16) $(55) - (21)$

17) $(-11) - (-5) - (10)$

18) $(50) - (-5) + (-25)$

19) $(4) - (-5) - (-3)$

20) $(12) - (3) - (-8)$

21) $(32) - (2) - (-20)$

22) $(-20) - (-44)$

23) $(-9) - 13 + 20$

24) $12 - (15) - (-13)$

Multiplying and Dividing Integers

✍ **Find each product.**

1) $(-8) \times (-5)$

2) 12×3

3) $(-2) \times 5 \times (-4)$

4) $4 \times (-5) \times (-6)$

5) $11 \times (-10)$

6) $32 \times (-4)$

7) 21×3

8) $(-12) \times (-4)$

9) $3 \times (-5) \times 7$

10) $6 \times (-4) \times 3$

11) $(-11) \times (-5)$

12) $(-4) \times (-3) \times 5$

✍ **Find each quotient.**

13) $72 \div 9$

14) $(-84) \div 7$

15) $(-95) \div (-5)$

16) $72 \div (+9)$

17) $39 \div 3$

18) $(-99) \div (-11)$

19) $22 \div (-11)$

20) $(-123) \div 1$

21) $60 \div 4$

22) $(-26) \div (-2)$

23) $(-44) \div (-11)$

24) $(-0) \div 15$

Arrange, Order, and Comparing Integers

✍ Order each set of integers from least to greatest.

1) 2, 6, – 15, – 11, 1   ___, ___, ___, ___, ___, ___

2) 9, – 8, 3, – 2 ,11   ___, ___, ___, ___, ___, ___

3) 36, – 12, 5, 1, – 2   ___, ___, ___, ___, ___, ___

4) 31, 18, 0, – 54, 9, – 5   ___, ___, ___, ___, ___, ___

5) – 15, –25, –37, 7, 0, 9   ___, ___, ___, ___, ___, ___

6) – 55, – 23, –11, 0, 3, 7   ___, ___, ___, ___, ___, ___

✍ Order each set of integers from greatest to least.

7) 1,17, 6, 8, 65, 2   ___, ___, ___, ___, ___, ___

8) – 12,6, –7, 2, – 11   ___, ___, ___, ___, ___, ___

9) – 14, 17, 7, 37, 9   ___, ___, ___, ___, ___, ___

10) – 54, 0, 14,19, 15   ___, ___, ___, ___, ___, ___

11) 12, 7, –1, – 11, 9, -3   ___, ___, ___, ___, ___, ___

12) – 14, – 7, 98, 29, 28, 3   ___, ___, ___, ___, ___, ___

✍ **Compare. Use >, =, <**

1) 4 _____ 3

2) – 22 _____ –11

3) 0 _____ – 31

4) –41 _____ –12

5) – 64 _____ –64

6) –1 42 _____ –1 48

7) 68 _____ 100

8) – 106 _____ – 106

9) 16 _____ – (– 16)

10) 405 _____ – 405

Order of Operations

✍ **Evaluate each expression.**

1) $24 - (8 \times 6)$

2) $5 \times 6 - \left(\dfrac{15}{11 - (-4)}\right)$

3) $12 - (6 \times (-3))$

4) $(6 \times 7) + (-7)$

5) $\left(\dfrac{(-1)+4}{(-1)+(-2)}\right) \times (-9)$

6) $(16 + (-4) - 2) \times 7 - 25$

7) $\dfrac{30}{2(9 - (-1)) - 10}$

8) $58 - (6 \times 9)$

9) $13 + (4 \times 2)$

10) $((-3) + 15) \div (-3)$

11) $[(-8 \div 2) \div (2 - 4))$

12) $34 + (-5) \times \left(\dfrac{(-12)}{10}\right)$

Integers and Absolute Value

✍ Write absolute value of each number.

1) 62

2) − 32

3) − 11

4) 5

5) 17

6) − 12

7) − 9

8) 0

9) -14

10) − 7

11) −33

12) 25

13) − 34

14) − 55

✍ Evaluate.

15) $|-12| - |3| + 2$

16) $19 + |-5 - 14| - |2|$

17) $38 - |-17| - 3$

18) $|26| - |-12| + 9$

19) $|91| - |-18| - 18$

20) $|13| - |-18| + 40$

21) $|-77 + 17| + 15 - 5$

22) $|-11| + |-9|$

23) $|-12 + 4 - 2| + |3 + 6|$

24) $|-40| - |-20| - 3$

25) $|-10 + 4| \times \frac{|-7 \times 5|}{7}$

26) $\frac{|-16 \times 3|}{2} \times |-12| =$

Answers of Worksheets – Chapter 1

Rounding

1) 90
2) 8.000
3) 4,000
4) 570

5) 1.3
6) 18.00
7) 2.000
8) 400

9) 14.2
10) 3,000
11) 4.300
12) 7.000

Rounding and Estimates

1) 40
2) 70
3) 260
4) 100
5) 280

6) 170
7) 190
8) 90
9) 150
10) 420

11) 1,310
12) 750
13) 10,900
14) 3,710
15) 5,650

Whole Number Addition and Subtraction

1) 117,000
2) 926
3) 1,800

4) 561
5) 440
6) 580

7) 9,350
8) 43,000

Whole Number Multiplication and Division

1) 720
2) 4,800
3) 18,000
4) 8,400
5) 10,000
6) 24,000

7) 15,050
8) 25
9) 9
10) 21
11) 32
12) 185

13) 275
14) 38
15) 462
16) 1,206

Adding and Subtracting Integers

1) − 15
2) − 3
3) 12
4) 30

5) 40
6) − 12
7) − 30
8) 9

9) − 27
10) 6
11) 30
12) 27

13) 20

14) −45

15) 50

16) 34

17) −16

18) 30

19) 12

20) 17

21) 50

22) 24

23) −2

24) 10

Multiplying and Dividing Integers

1) 40

2) 36

3) 40

4) 120

5) − 110

6) − 128

7) 63

8) 48

9) 105

10) −72

11) 55

12) 60

13) 8

14) − 12

15) 19

16) 8

17) 13

18) 9

19) −2

20) −123

21) 15

22) 13

23) 4

24) 0

Arrange and Order, Comparing Integers

1) − 15, − 11, 1, 2, 6

2) − 8, − 2, 3, 9 ,11

3) − 12, − 2, 1, 5, 36

4) −54, −5, 0, 9, 18, 31

5) − 37, − 25, −15, 0, 7, 9

6) −55, −23, −11, 0, 3 ,7

7) 65, 17, 8, 6, 2, 1

8) 6, 2, − 7, − 11, − 12

9) 37, 17, 9, 7, −14

10) 19, 15, 14, 0, −54

11) 12, 9, 7, −1, −3, −11

12) 98, 29, 28, 3, −7, −14

Compare.

1) >

2) <

3) >

4) <

5) =

6) >

7) <

8) =

9) =

10) >

Order of Operations

1) −24

2) 29

3) 30

4) 35

5) 9

6) 45

7) 3

8) 4

9) 21

10) −4

11) 2

12) 40

Integers and Absolute Value

1) 62	10) 7	19) 55
2) 32	11) 33	20) 35
3) 11	12) 25	21) 70
4) 5	13) 34	22) 20
5) 17	14) 55	23) 19
6) 12	15) 11	24) 17
7) 9	16) 36	25) 30
8) 0	17) 18	26) 288
9) 14	18) 23	

Chapter 2: Fractions and Decimals

Topics that you'll learn in this chapter:

➢ Simplifying Fractions

➢ Adding and Subtracting Fractions, Mixed Numbers and Decimals

➢ Multiplying and Dividing Fractions, Mixed Numbers and Decimals

➢ Comparing and Rounding Decimals

➢ Converting Between Fractions, Decimals and Mixed Numbers

➢ Factoring Numbers, Greatest Common Factor, and Least Common

   Multiple

➢ Divisibility Rules

"A Man is like a fraction whose numerator is what he is and whose denominator is what he thinks of himself. The larger the denominator, the smaller the fraction." –Tolstoy

Simplifying Fractions

✎ Simplify the fractions.

1) $\dfrac{44}{64}$

2) $\dfrac{12}{26}$

3) $\dfrac{15}{25}$

4) $\dfrac{30}{45}$

5) $\dfrac{18}{27}$

6) $\dfrac{30}{90}$

7) $\dfrac{14}{36}$

8) $\dfrac{24}{58}$

9) $\dfrac{30}{90}$

10) $\dfrac{6}{54}$

11) $\dfrac{35}{55}$

12) $\dfrac{28}{38}$

13) $5\dfrac{40}{64}$

14) $2\dfrac{24}{42}$

15) $9\dfrac{5}{35}$

16) $3\dfrac{45}{75}$

17) $1\dfrac{62}{124}$

18) $4\dfrac{12}{66}$

19) $1\dfrac{55}{70}$

20) $\dfrac{54}{60}$

21) $7\dfrac{68}{136}$

Factoring Numbers

List all positive factors of each number.

1) 90

2) 12

3) 49

4) 100

5) 50

6) 64

7) 34

8) 27

9) 63

10) 110

11) 96

12) 48

List the prime factorization for each number.

13) 40

14) 210

15) 105

16) 24

17) 42

18) 66

19) 78

20) 165

21) 125

22) 32

23) 12

24) 23

25) 60

26) 54

Greatest Common Factor (GCF)

✍ Find the GCF for each number pair.

1) 12, 25

2) 24, 36

3) 9, 36

4) 27, 12

5) 54, 39

6) 66, 77

7) 18, 24

8) 80, 130

9) 60, 80

10) 21, 14

11) 64, 32

12) 90, 45

13) 72, 84

14) 30, 45

15) 63, 42

16) 125,50

17) 36, 52

18) 165, 60

Least Common Multiple (LCM)

✍ Find the LCM for each number pair.

1) 12, 18

2) 15, 30

3) 60, 40

4) 14, 28

5) 24, 32

6) 40, 20

7) 84, 60

8) 42, 18

9) 52, 78

10) 15, 12

11) 72, 6

12) 10, 30, 60

13) 12, 18, 24

14) 10, 15, 35

15) 14, 27, 54

16) 3, 11, 13

17) 14, 7, 42

18) 72, 66, 24

Divisibility Rules

✍ **Use the divisibility rules to find the factors of each number.**

1) 12   2 3 4 5 6 7 8 9

2) 24   2 3 4 5 6 7 8 9

3) 36   2 3 4 5 6 7 8 9

4) 18   2 3 4 5 6 7 8 9

5) 30   2 3 4 5 6 7 8 9

6) 54   2 3 4 5 6 7 8 9

7) 64   2 3 4 5 6 7 8 9

8) 42   2 3 4 5 6 7 8 9

9) 90   2 3 4 5 6 7 8 9

10) 80   2 3 4 5 6 7 8 9

11) 72   2 3 4 5 6 7 8 9

12) 84   2 3 4 5 6 7 8 9

Adding and Subtracting Fractions

✎ **Add fractions.**

1) $\dfrac{1}{4} + \dfrac{2}{3}$

4) $\dfrac{2}{15} + \dfrac{4}{15}$

7) $\dfrac{3}{4} + \dfrac{1}{2}$

2) $\dfrac{1}{3} + \dfrac{1}{2}$

5) $\dfrac{1}{12} + \dfrac{2}{3}$

8) $\dfrac{6}{7} + \dfrac{3}{21}$

3) $\dfrac{1}{4} + \dfrac{5}{7}$

6) $\dfrac{3}{7} + \dfrac{2}{3}$

9) $\dfrac{5}{13} + \dfrac{1}{2}$

✎ **Subtract fractions.**

10) $\dfrac{1}{2} - \dfrac{1}{5}$

13) $\dfrac{2}{3} - \dfrac{2}{7}$

16) $\dfrac{3}{4} - \dfrac{1}{3}$

11) $\dfrac{1}{7} - \dfrac{1}{9}$

14) $\dfrac{8}{15} - \dfrac{1}{5}$

17) $\dfrac{1}{3} - \dfrac{1}{4}$

12) $\dfrac{3}{5} - \dfrac{1}{15}$

15) $\dfrac{3}{8} - \dfrac{2}{12}$

18) $\dfrac{6}{5} - \dfrac{5}{6}$

Multiplying and Dividing Fractions

✎ **Multiplying fractions. Then simplify.**

1) $\dfrac{3}{5} \times \dfrac{5}{9}$

2) $\dfrac{6}{49} \times \dfrac{7}{3}$

3) $\dfrac{5}{21} \times \dfrac{7}{10}$

4) $\dfrac{8}{33} \times \dfrac{11}{24}$

5) $\dfrac{3}{29} \times \dfrac{29}{3}$

6) $0 \times \dfrac{103}{28}$

7) $\dfrac{8}{11} \times 11$

8) $\dfrac{2}{5} \times \dfrac{10}{3}$

9) $\dfrac{7}{9} \times \dfrac{12}{28}$

10) $\dfrac{13}{5} \times \dfrac{15}{26}$

✎ **Dividing fractions.**

11) $3 \div \dfrac{9}{7}$

12) $\dfrac{4}{9} \div 4$

13) $0 \div \dfrac{2}{5}$

14) $\dfrac{32}{25} \div \dfrac{8}{5}$

15) $\dfrac{5}{21} \div \dfrac{2}{21}$

16) $\dfrac{2}{7} \div \dfrac{8}{35}$

17) $\dfrac{3}{5} \div \dfrac{4}{5}$

18) $\dfrac{12}{25} \div \dfrac{3}{5}$

19) $\dfrac{3}{8} \div \dfrac{2}{5}$

20) $7 \div \dfrac{2}{3}$

21) $\dfrac{6}{7} \div \dfrac{9}{28}$

22) $\dfrac{5}{32} \div \dfrac{3}{16}$

Adding and Subtracting Mixed Numbers

✎ **Add.**

1) $2\frac{1}{3}+1\frac{2}{3}$

2) $3\frac{1}{2}+1\frac{1}{4}$

3) $1\frac{1}{7}+2\frac{1}{3}$

4) $1\frac{1}{2}+3\frac{2}{3}$

5) $1\frac{2}{5}+2\frac{1}{10}$

6) $7+2\frac{1}{2}$

7) $4\frac{1}{3}+2\frac{2}{3}$

8) $2\frac{2}{3}+1\frac{1}{4}$

9) $2\frac{3}{4}+3\frac{1}{8}$

10) $9+1\frac{1}{9}$

11) $4\frac{5}{12}+2\frac{3}{4}$

12) $3\frac{1}{7}+2\frac{3}{14}$

✎ **Subtract.**

1) $5\frac{2}{7}-2\frac{1}{14}$

2) $4\frac{2}{5}-\frac{2}{3}$

3) $3\frac{3}{7}-1\frac{1}{14}$

4) $7\frac{2}{5}-5\frac{1}{3}$

5) $4\frac{1}{2}-1\frac{3}{2}$

6) $5\frac{2}{3}-2\frac{4}{3}$

7) $7\frac{5}{12}-5\frac{7}{12}$

8) $5\frac{2}{9}-2\frac{1}{18}$

9) $3\frac{2}{5}-2\frac{1}{5}$

10) $3\frac{4}{9}-1\frac{2}{9}$

11) $7\frac{4}{5}-3\frac{1}{4}$

12) $4\frac{1}{12}-3\frac{1}{18}$

Multiplying and Dividing Mixed Numbers

✎ **Find each product.**

1) $2\frac{1}{3} \times \frac{1}{2}$

2) $1\frac{2}{5} \times \frac{2}{3}$

3) $2\frac{4}{3} \times 2\frac{2}{6}$

4) $2\frac{1}{2} \times 1\frac{2}{4}$

5) $3\frac{1}{2} \times 1\frac{2}{3}$

6) $1\frac{1}{7} \times 1\frac{3}{4}$

7) $1\frac{1}{4} \times 2\frac{6}{5}$

8) $3\frac{1}{2} \times 4\frac{2}{5}$

9) $1\frac{2}{5} \times 2\frac{1}{3}$

10) $2\frac{1}{3} \times 1\frac{3}{2}$

11) $3\frac{1}{3} \times 2\frac{1}{2}$

12) $2\frac{2}{3} \times 3\frac{3}{5}$

✎ **Find each quotient.**

1) $2\frac{2}{3} \div 1\frac{3}{7}$

2) $1\frac{2}{5} \div 2\frac{1}{3}$

3) $2\frac{3}{5} \div 1\frac{3}{8}$

4) $\frac{3}{2} \div 2\frac{3}{4}$

5) $1\frac{4}{7} \div 2\frac{2}{3}$

6) $1\frac{2}{3} \div 2\frac{1}{3}$

7) $0 \div 4\frac{2}{5}$

8) $2\frac{2}{5} \div 1\frac{1}{2}$

9) $1\frac{2}{3} \div 2\frac{1}{5}$

10) $3\frac{2}{7} \div 4\frac{3}{5}$

11) $1\frac{1}{4} \div 2\frac{4}{5}$

12) $2 \div 3\frac{1}{3}$

Comparing Decimals

Write the correct comparison symbol (>, < or =).

1) 0.025 _____ 0.25

2) 0.9 _____ 0.888

3) 4.510 _____ 4.150

4) 1 0.01 _____ 10.10

5) 0.987 _____ 0.991

6) 0.321 _____ 0.421

7) 5.210 _____ 5.211

8) 9.64 _____ 9.640

9) 43.012 _____ 43.030

10) 4.101 _____ 4.001

11) 5.012 _____ 5.010

12) 0.050 _____ 0.05

13) 5.120 _____ 5.212

14) 2.54 _____ 2.045

15) 1.490 _____ 1.049

16) 18.004 _____ 18.040

17) 0.020 _____ 0.20

18) 0.071 _____ 0.700

19) 0.08 _____ 0.009

20) 0.690 _____ 0.609

Rounding Decimals

Round each decimal number to the nearest place indicated.

1) 1.8<u>2</u>

2) 0.9<u>4</u>

3) 12.<u>6</u>63

4) 4.<u>6</u>77

5) <u>2</u>.907

6) 0.9<u>8</u>9

7) 11.<u>1</u>4

8) 13.<u>8</u>

9) 7.9<u>1</u>9

10) 8.<u>6</u>95

11) 6.0<u>8</u>

12) 12.<u>2</u>67

13) 9.<u>3</u>01

14) 10.07<u>1</u>

15) 5<u>5</u>.89

16) 5<u>9</u>.15

17) 3<u>2</u>9.018

18) 92.<u>4</u>10

19) 1.4<u>9</u>9

20) 2<u>5</u>.15

21) 67.7<u>0</u>9

22) 173.<u>1</u>83

23) 32.<u>2</u>81

24) 4.<u>0</u>94

25) 0.0<u>3</u>21

26) 10.<u>4</u>69

27) 2.<u>2</u>91

Adding and Subtracting Decimals

✎Add and subtract decimals.

1)
$$
\begin{array}{r}
87.15 \\
-\ 32.35 \\
\hline

\end{array}
$$

4)
$$
\begin{array}{r}
65.23 \\
-\ 56.48 \\
\hline

\end{array}
$$

2)
$$
\begin{array}{r}
90.43 \\
+\ 44.09 \\
\hline

\end{array}
$$

5)
$$
\begin{array}{r}
98.125 \\
+\ 58.54 \\
\hline

\end{array}
$$

3)
$$
\begin{array}{r}
58.56 \\
+\ 12.10 \\
\hline

\end{array}
$$

6)
$$
\begin{array}{r}
162.05 \\
-\ 83.65 \\
\hline

\end{array}
$$

✎Solve.

7) ___ + 5.0 = 9.08

10) 32.12 − ___ = 12.07

8) 7.06 + ___ = 24.6

11) ___ + 0.156 = 3.054

9) 21.9 − ___ = 6.9

12) ___ − 5.33 = 21.98

Multiplying and Dividing Decimals

Find each product

1)
$$\begin{array}{r} 1.5 \\ \times\ 0.16 \\ \hline \end{array}$$

4)
$$\begin{array}{r} 3.19 \\ \times\ 21.5 \\ \hline \end{array}$$

7)
$$\begin{array}{r} 5.0 \\ \times\ 1.4 \\ \hline \end{array}$$

2)
$$\begin{array}{r} 5.3 \\ \times\ 1.9 \\ \hline \end{array}$$

5)
$$\begin{array}{r} 9.3 \\ \times\ 11.5 \\ \hline \end{array}$$

8)
$$\begin{array}{r} 23.8 \\ \times\ 10 \\ \hline \end{array}$$

3)
$$\begin{array}{r} 0.06 \\ \times\ 2.5 \\ \hline \end{array}$$

6)
$$\begin{array}{r} 3.01 \\ \times\ 2.1 \\ \hline \end{array}$$

9)
$$\begin{array}{r} 21.5 \\ \times\ 10 \\ \hline \end{array}$$

Find each quotient.

10) $25.7 \div 0.5$

11) $67.2 \div 4$

12) $61.75 \div 1.9$

13) $18.0 \div 1.2$

14) $12.4 \div 10$

15) $2.2 \div 100$

16) $1.88 \div 100$

17) $55.1 \div 100$

18) $0.1 \div 100$

19) $0.25 \div 10$

Converting Between Fractions, Decimals and Mixed Numbers

✎ Convert fractions to decimals.

1) $\dfrac{25}{100}$

4) $\dfrac{4}{12}$

7) $\dfrac{12}{48}$

2) $\dfrac{4}{10}$

5) $\dfrac{5}{16}$

8) $\dfrac{20}{25}$

3) $\dfrac{3}{8}$

6) $\dfrac{60}{100}$

9) $\dfrac{26}{80}$

✎ Convert decimal into fraction or mixed numbers.

10) 0.25

14) 3.5

18) 0.15

11) 8.25

15) 0.5

19) 0.07

12) 0.12

16) 3.6

20) 2.7

13) 0.75

17) 0.07

21) 2.5

Answers of Worksheets – Chapter 2

Simplifying Fractions

1) $\frac{11}{16}$

2) $\frac{6}{13}$

3) $\frac{3}{5}$

4) $\frac{2}{3}$

5) $\frac{2}{3}$

6) $\frac{1}{3}$

7) $\frac{7}{18}$

8) $\frac{12}{29}$

9) $\frac{1}{3}$

10) $\frac{1}{9}$

11) $\frac{7}{11}$

12) $\frac{14}{19}$

13) $5\frac{5}{8}$

14) $2\frac{12}{21}$

15) $9\frac{1}{7}$

16) $3\frac{3}{5}$

17) $1\frac{1}{2}$

18) $4\frac{2}{11}$

19) $1\frac{11}{14}$

20) $\frac{9}{10}$

21) $7\frac{1}{2}$

Factoring Numbers

1) $1, 2, 3, 5, 6, 9, 10, 15, 18, 30, 45, 90$

2) $1, 2, 3, 4, 6, 12$

3) $1, 7, 49$

4) $1, 2, 5, 10, 20, 25, 50, 100$

5) $1, 2, 5, 10, 25, 50$

6) $1, 2, 4, 8, 16, 32, 64$

7) $1, 2, 17, 34$

8) $1, 3, 9, 27$

9) $1, 3, 7, 9, 21, 63$

10) $1, 2, 5, 10, 11, 22, 55, 110$

11) $1, 2, 3, 4, 6, 8, 12, 16, 24, 32, 48, 96$

12) $1, 2, 3, 4, 6, 8, 12, 16, 24, 48$

13) $2 \times 2 \times 2 \times 5$

14) $2 \times 3 \times 5 \times 7$

15) $3 \times 5 \times 7$

16) $2 \times 2 \times 2 \times 3$

17) $2 \times 3 \times 7$

18) $2 \times 3 \times 11$

19) $2 \times 3 \times 13$

20) $3 \times 5 \times 11$

21) $5 \times 5 \times 5$

22) $2 \times 2 \times 2 \times 2 \times 2$

23) $2 \times 2 \times 3$

24) 23×1

25) $2 \times 2 \times 3 \times 5$

26) $2 \times 3 \times 3 \times 3$

Greatest Common Factor

1) 1

2) 12

3) 9

4) 3

5) 3

6) 11

7) 6

8) 10

9) 20

10) 7

11) 32

12) 45

13) 12

14) 15

15) 21

16) 25

17) 4

18) 15

Least Common Multiple

1) 36

2) 30

3) 120

4) 28

5) 96

6) 40

7) 420

8) 126

9) 156

10) 60

11) 72

12) 60

13) 72

14) 210

15) 378

16) 429

17) 42

18) 792

Divisibility Rules

1) 12   <u>2</u> <u>3</u> <u>4</u> 5 <u>6</u> 7 8 9 10

2) 24   <u>2</u> <u>3</u> <u>4</u> 5 <u>6</u> 7 <u>8</u> 9 10

3) 36   <u>2</u> <u>3</u> 4 5 <u>6</u> 7 8 <u>9</u> 10

4) 18   <u>2</u> <u>3</u> 4 5 <u>6</u> 7 8 <u>9</u> 10

5) 30   <u>2</u> <u>3</u> 4 <u>5</u> <u>6</u> 7 8 9 <u>10</u>

6) 54   <u>2</u> <u>3</u> 4 5 <u>6</u> 7 8 <u>9</u> 10

7) 64   2 3 <u>4</u> 5 6 7 <u>8</u> 9 10

8) 42   <u>2</u> <u>3</u> 4 5 <u>6</u> <u>7</u> 8 9 10

9) 90   <u>2</u> <u>3</u> 4 <u>5</u> <u>6</u> 7 8 <u>9</u> <u>10</u>

10) 80   2 3 <u>4</u> <u>5</u> 6 7 <u>8</u> 9 <u>10</u>

11) 72   <u>2</u> <u>3</u> <u>4</u> 5 <u>6</u> 7 <u>8</u> <u>9</u> 10

12) 84   <u>2</u> <u>3</u> <u>4</u> 5 <u>6</u> <u>7</u> 8 9 10

Adding and Subtracting Fractions

1) $\frac{11}{12}$

2) $\frac{5}{6}$

3) $\frac{27}{28}$

4) $\frac{2}{5}$

5) $\frac{3}{4}$

6) $1\frac{2}{21}$

7) $1\frac{1}{4}$

8) 1

9) $\frac{23}{26}$

10) $\frac{3}{10}$

11) $\frac{2}{63}$

12) $\frac{8}{15}$

13) $\frac{8}{21}$

14) $\frac{1}{3}$

15) $\frac{5}{24}$

16) $\frac{5}{12}$

17) $\frac{1}{12}$

18) $\frac{11}{30}$

Multiplying and Dividing Fractions

1) $\frac{1}{3}$

2) $\frac{2}{7}$

3) $\frac{1}{6}$

4) $\frac{1}{9}$

5) 1

6) 0

7) 8

8) $1\frac{1}{3}$

9) $\frac{1}{3}$

10) $1\frac{1}{2}$

11) $\frac{7}{3}$

12) $\frac{1}{9}$

13) 0

14) $\frac{4}{5}$

15) $2\frac{1}{2}$

16) $1\frac{1}{4}$

17) $\frac{3}{4}$

18) $\frac{4}{5}$

19) $\frac{15}{16}$

20) $10\frac{1}{2}$

21) $2\frac{2}{3}$

22) $\frac{5}{6}$

Adding Mixed Numbers

1) 4

2) $4\frac{3}{4}$

3) $3\frac{10}{21}$

4) $5\frac{1}{6}$

5) $3\frac{1}{2}$

6) $9\frac{1}{2}$

7) 7

8) $3\frac{11}{12}$

9) $5\frac{7}{8}$

10) $10\frac{1}{9}$

11) $7\frac{1}{6}$

12) $5\frac{5}{14}$

Subtract Mixed Numbers

1) $3\frac{3}{14}$

2) $3\frac{11}{15}$

3) $2\frac{5}{14}$

4) $2\frac{1}{15}$

5) 2

6) $2\frac{1}{3}$

7) $1\frac{5}{6}$

8) $3\frac{1}{6}$

9) $1\frac{1}{5}$

10) $2\frac{2}{9}$

11) $4\frac{11}{20}$

12) $1\frac{1}{36}$

Multiplying Mixed Numbers

1) $1\frac{1}{6}$

2) $\frac{14}{15}$

3) $7\frac{7}{9}$

4) $3\frac{3}{4}$

5) $5\frac{5}{6}$

6) 2

7) 4

8) $15\frac{2}{5}$

9) $3\frac{4}{15}$

10) $5\frac{5}{6}$ 11) $8\frac{1}{3}$ 12) $9\frac{3}{5}$

Dividing Mixed Numbers

1) $1\frac{13}{15}$ 5) $\frac{33}{56}$ 9) $\frac{25}{33}$

2) $\frac{3}{5}$ 6) $\frac{5}{7}$ 10) $\frac{5}{7}$

3) $1\frac{49}{55}$ 7) 0 11) $\frac{25}{56}$

4) $\frac{6}{11}$ 8) $1\frac{3}{5}$ 12) $\frac{3}{5}$

Comparing Decimals

1) <   6) <   11) >   16) <

2) >   7) <   12) =   17) <

3) >   8) =   13) <   18) <

4) <   9) <   14) >   19) >

5) <   10) >   15) >   20) >

Rounding Decimals

1) 2.0   10) 8.7   19) 1.5

2) 1.0   11) 6.1   20) 25

3) 13   12) 12.3   21) 67.71

4) 5   13) 9.3   22) 173.2

5) 3   14) 10.07   23) 32.2

6) 0.1   15) 56   24) 4.1

7) 11.1   16) 59   25) 0.03

8) 14   17) 330   26) 10.5

9) 7.92   18) 92   27) 2.3

Adding and Subtracting Decimals

1) 54.8   5) 156.665   9) 15

2) 134.52   6) 78.4   10) 20.05

3) 70.66   7) 4.08   11) 2.898

4) 8.75   8) 17.54   12) 27.31

Multiplying and Dividing Decimals

1) 0.24   2) 10.07   3) 0.15

4) 68.585

5) 106.95

6) 6.321

7) 7

8) 238

9) 215

10) 51.4

11) 16.8

12) 32.5

13) 15

14) 1.24

15) 0.022

16) 0.0188

17) 0.551

18) 0.001

19) 0.025

Converting Between Fractions, Decimals and Mixed Numbers

1) 0.25

2) 0.4

3) 0.375

4) 0.333

5) 0.3125

6) 0.6

7) 0.25

8) 0.8

9) 0.325

10) $\frac{1}{4}$

11) $8\frac{1}{4}$

12) $\frac{3}{25}$

13) $\frac{3}{4}$

14) $3\frac{1}{2}$

15) $\frac{1}{2}$

16) $3\frac{3}{5}$

17) $\frac{7}{100}$

18) $\frac{15}{100}$

19) $\frac{7}{100}$

20) $\frac{27}{10}$

21) $2\frac{1}{2}$

Chapter 3: Proportion, Ratio, Percent

Topics that you'll learn in this chapter:

- ➢ Writing and Simplifying Ratios
- ➢ Create a Proportion
- ➢ Similar Figures
- ➢ Simple Interest
- ➢ Ratio and Rates Word Problems
- ➢ Percentage Calculations
- ➢ Converting Between Percent, Fractions, and Decimals
- ➢ Percent Problems
- ➢ Markup, Discount, and Tax

"Do not worry about your difficulties in mathematics. I can assure you mine are still greater." – *Albert Einstein*

Writing and Simplifying Ratios

✎ **Express each ratio as a rate and unite rate.**

1) 80 dollars for 4 chairs.

2) 125miles on 25 gallons of gas.

3) 147 miles on 7 hours

4) 12 inches of snow in 24 hours

5) 14 dimes to 112 dimes

6) 30 feet out of 90 feet

✎ **Express each ratio as a fraction in the simplest form.**

7) 13 cups to 39 cups

8) 17 cakes out of 51 cakes

9) 35 red desks out of 125 desks

10) 8 story books out of 32 books

11) 12 gallons to 20 gallons

12) 11 miles out of 121 miles

✎ **Reduce each ratio.**

1) 49: 14

2) 35: 25

3) 16: 36

4) 4: 60

5) 8: 64

6) 22: 55

7) 18: 99

8) 64: 72

9) 70: 40

10) 16: 24

11) 14: 22

12) 5: 45

13) 15: 45

14) 18: 81

15) 32: 56

16) 10: 55

17) 12: 24

18) 23:115

Create a Proportion

✎ Create proportion from the given set of numbers

1) 3, 2, 9, 6

2) 5, 11, 25,55

3) 49, 7, 12, 84

4) 20, 10, 200, 1

5) 4, 2, 16, 32

6) 4, 18, 12, 6

7) 24, 7, 21, 8

8) 15, 12, 30, 24

9) 9, 27, 81, 3

Similar Figures

✎ Each pair of figures is similar. Find the missing side.

1)

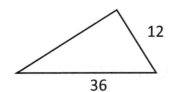

2)

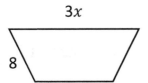

3)

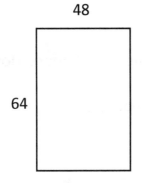

Ratio and Rates Word Problems

✍ Solve.

1) In Peter's class, 21 of the students are tall and 9 are short. In Elise's class 56 students are tall and 24 students are short. Which class has a higher ratio of tall to short students?

2) In a party, 8 soft drinks are required for every 35 guests. If there are 560 guests, how many soft drinks is required?

3) The price of 5 bananas at the first Market is $1.05. The price of 7 of the same bananas at second Market is $1.07. Which place is the better buy?

4) You can buy 6 cans of green beans at a supermarket for $3.50. How much does it cost to buy 42 cans of green beans?

5) The bakers at a Bakery can make 110 bagels in 4 hours. How many bagels can they bake in 6 hours? What is that rate per hour?

Percentage Calculations

✎ Calculate the percentages.

1) 75% of 45

2) 50% of 66

3) 90% of 58

4) 25% of 88

5) 5% of 100

6) 80% of 60

7) 15% of 45

8) 18% of 90

9) 20% of 70

10) 12% of 25

11) 25% of 75

12) 75% of 18

13) 30% of 50

14) 10% of 85

15) 5% of 90

16) 50% of 10

✎ Solve.

17) What percentage of 60 is 6

18) 6.76 is what percentage of 52?

19) 17 is what percentage of 85?

20) Find what percentage of 96 is 24.

Percent Problems

✎ **Solve each problem.**

1) 52% of what number is 13?

2) What is 15% of 9 inches?

3) What percent of 185.6 is 23.2?

4) 24 is 72% of what?

5) 35 is what percent of 70?

6) 10 is 200% of what?

7) 14 is what percent of 70?

8) 26% of 100 is what number?

9) Mia require 50% to pass. If she gets 250 marks and falls short by 90 marks, what were the maximum marks she could have got?

10) Jack scored 14 out of 70 marks in mathematics, 9 out of 10 marks in history and 56 out of 100 marks in science. In which subject his percentage of marks is the best?

Markup, Discount, and Tax

✎ **Find the selling price of each item.**

1) Cost of a chair: $20, markup: 30%, discount: 10%, tax: 10%

2) Cost of computer: $1,600.00, markup: 65%

3) Cost of a pen: $3.20, markup: 50%, discount: 15%, tax: 5%

4) Cost of a puppy: $1,800, markup: 40%, discount: 10%

Simple Interest

✍ **Use simple interest to find the ending balance.**

1) $1,200 at 15% for 3 years.

2) $320,000 at 2.85% for 7 years.

3) $1,500 at 2.25% for 12 years.

4) $12,500 at 6.2% for 4 years.

5) $31,000 at 1.5% for 10 months.

6) Emily puts $6,000 into an investment yielding 3.25% annual simple interest; she left the money in for 3 years. How much interest does Sara get at the end of those 3 years?

7) A new car, valued at $42,000, depreciates at 7.5% per year from original price. Find the value of the car 6 years after purchase.

8) $880 interest is earned on a principal of $2,200 at a simple interest rate of 4% interest per year. For how many years was the principal invested?

Converting Between Percent, Fractions, and Decimals

✎ Converting fractions to decimals

1) $\dfrac{23}{10}$

2) $\dfrac{2}{20}$

3) $\dfrac{7}{100}$

4) $\dfrac{20}{50}$

5) $\dfrac{3}{60}$

6) $\dfrac{15}{10}$

7) $\dfrac{3}{10}$

8) $\dfrac{13}{26}$

9) $\dfrac{8}{100}$

✎ Write each decimal as a percent.

10) 2.15

11) 0.26

12) 1.09

13) 0.51

14) 0.025

15) 0.002

16) 0.08

17) 0.2

18) 3.25

19) 1.01

Answers of Worksheets – Chapter 3

Writing Ratios

1) $\frac{80 \text{ dollars}}{4 \text{ books}}$, 20.00 dollars per chair

2) $\frac{125 \text{ miles}}{25 \text{ gallons}}$, 5 miles per gallon

3) $\frac{147 \text{ miles}}{7 \text{ hours}}$, 21 miles per hour

4) $\frac{12" \text{ of snow}}{24 \text{ hours}}$, 0.5 inches of snow per hour

5) $\frac{14 \text{ dimes}}{112 \text{ dimes}}$, $\frac{1}{8}$ per dime

6) $\frac{30 \text{ feet}}{90 \text{ feet}}$, $\frac{1}{3}$ per foot

7)

8) $\frac{1}{3}$

9) $\frac{7}{25}$

10) $\frac{1}{4}$

11) $\frac{3}{5}$

12) $\frac{1}{11}$

Reduce each Ratio

1) 7: 2

2) 7: 5

3) 4: 9

4) 1: 15

5) 1: 8

6) 2: 5

7) 2: 11

8) 8: 9

9) 7: 4

10) 2: 3

11) 7: 11

12) 1: 9

13) 1: 3

14) 2: 9

15) 4: 7

16) 2: 11

17) 1: 2

18) 1: 5

Create a Proportion

1) 2: 6 = 3: 9

2) 5: 25 = 11: 55

3) 7: 49 = 12: 84

4) 1: 10 = 20: 200

5) 2: 16=4: 32

6) 4: 12 =6: 18

7) 8: 24 =7: 21

8) 12: 24 =15: 30

9) 3: 27 =9: 81

Similar Figures

1) 6

2) 4

3) 2

Ratio and Rates Word Problems

1) The ratio for both classes is equal to 7 to 3.

2) 128

3) The price at the second Market is a better buy.

4) $24.5

5) 165, the rate is 27.5 per hour.

Percentage Calculations

1) 33.75	6) 48	11) 18.75	16) 5
2) 33	7) 6.75	12) 13.5	17) 10%
3) 52.2	8) 16.2	13) 15	18) 13%
4) 22	9) 14	14) 8.5	19) 20%
5) 5	10) 3	15) 4.5	20) 25%

Percent Problems

1) 25	5) 50%	9) 680
2) 60	6) 5	10) history
3) 12.5	7) 20%	
4) 33.33	8) 26	

Markup, Discount, and Tax

1) $25.74	3) $4.284
2) $2,640	4) $2,268

Simple Interest

1) $1740	4) $15600	7) $23,100
2) $383,840.00	5) $31,387.50	8) 10 years
3) $1,905.00	6) $585.00	

Converting Between Percent, Fractions, and Decimals

1) 2.3	8) 0.5	15) 0.2%
2) 0.01	9) 0.08	16) 8%
3) 0.07	10) 215%	17) 20%
4) 0.4	11) 26%	18) 325%
5) 0.05	12) 109%	19) 101%
6) 1.5	13) 51%	
7) 0.3	14) 2.5%	

Chapter 4: Exponents and Radicals

Topics that you'll learn in this chapter:

- ➤ Multiplication Property of Exponents

- ➤ Division Property of Exponents

- ➤ Powers of Products and Quotients

- ➤ Zero, Negative Exponents and Bases

"Mathematics is no more computation than typing is literature." – John Allen Paulos

Multiplication Property of Exponents

✍ **Simplify.**

1) $4^3 \times 4^2$

2) $2 \cdot 2^2 \cdot 2^3$

3) $2^4 \cdot 2$

4) $8x^2 \cdot x$

5) $15x^7 \cdot x$

6) $3x \cdot x^3$

7) $2x^5 \cdot 5x^4$

8) $5x^2 \cdot 3x^2y^2$

9) $6y^5 \cdot 8xy^2$

10) $5xy^3 \cdot 4x^3y^2$

11) $(2x^3)^2$

12) $2x^4y \cdot 3x^2y^2$

13) $6x \cdot 5y^4x^2 \cdot 2yx^3$

14) $(x^3)^3$

15) $(3x^2)^3$

16) $2x^3y^5 \cdot 2xy^2$

Division Property of Exponents

✍ **Simplify.**

1) $\dfrac{4^3}{4}$

2) $\dfrac{51}{51^{14}}$

3) $\dfrac{5^2}{5^3}$

4) $\dfrac{3^4}{3^1}$

5) $\dfrac{x}{x^7}$

6) $\dfrac{42x^2}{6x^2}$

7) $\dfrac{3x^{-3}}{12x^{-1}}$

8) $\dfrac{81x^5}{9x^3}$

9) $\dfrac{3x^4}{4x^5}$

10) $\dfrac{21x}{3x^2}$

14) $\dfrac{14x}{7y^5}$

18) $\dfrac{3x^4}{7x^5y^4}$

11) $\dfrac{3x}{7x^4}$

15) $\dfrac{2xy^5}{x^5y}$

19) $\dfrac{yx^3}{5yx^3}$

12) $\dfrac{2x^2}{3x^6}$

16) $\dfrac{2x^2}{5x}$

20) $\dfrac{3x^4}{2x^5}$

13) $\dfrac{18x^3}{10x^5}$

17) $\dfrac{8x^2y}{x^3}$

21) $\dfrac{x^7}{3x^7}$

Powers of Products and Quotients

🖉 Simplify.

1) $(2x^2)^3$

8) $(2x^3y)^4$

15) $(11x^9y^3)^2$

2) $(xy)^2$

9) $(7x^4y^8)^2$

16) $(6x^5\,y^3)^2$

3) $(5x^3)^2$

10) $(10x)^3$

17) $(3\,x^3\,)^5$

4) $(9x^3)^2$

11) $(x^5)^3$

18) $(7x^3)^2$

5) $(4x^2y^3)^2$

12) $(8x^{10}y^2)^3$

19) $(2x\,4y^4)^2$

6) $(5x^2y^3)^2$

13) $(9x^2x^2)^2$

20) $(6xy)^3$

7) $(2xy^2)^3$

14) $(2x^2\,8x)^2$

21) $(15x^2y^3)^2$

Zero and Negative Exponents

⊠Evaluate the following expressions.

1) 4^{-2}

2) 5^{-2}

3) 6^{-2}

4) 3^{-4}

5) 10^{-1}

6) 33^{-1}

7) 6^{-1}

8) 3^{-2}

9) 9^{-2}

10) 4^{-1}

11) 5^{-3}

12) 2^{-5}

13) 11^{-2}

14) 2^{-4}

15) 7^{-2}

16) 2^{-3}

17) 2^{-2}

18) 9^{-1}

19) 4^{-3}

20) 10^{-4}

21) $(\frac{2}{3})^{-2}$

22) $(\frac{1}{3})^{-2}$

23) $(\frac{1}{2})^{-3}$

24) $(\frac{6}{5})^{-2}$

25) 11^{-2}

26) 3^{-1}

Negative Exponents and Negative Bases

⊠Simplify.

1) 7^{-1}

2) $-2x^{-2}$

3) $\frac{x}{x^{-5}}$

4) $-\frac{a^{-2}}{b^{-1}}$

5) $\frac{7}{x^{-5}}$

6) $\frac{2b}{-5c^{-2}}$

7) $\frac{2n^{-1}}{12p^{-2}}$

8) $\frac{8b^{-4}}{3c^{-2}}$

9) $89xy^{-2}$

10) $(\frac{1}{3})^{-2}$

11) $(\frac{6}{7})^{-2}$

12) $(\frac{x}{4yz})^{-2}$

Writing Scientific Notation

✎ Write each number in scientific notation.

1) 25×10^3

2) 12

3) 0.0015

4) 54,000

5) 0.0051

6) 666

7) 0.0076

8) 2900

9) 100,000

10) 3,600,000

11) 60,000,000

12) 150

13) 0.108

14) 20

15) 260

16) 1,000,000

17) 0.00015

18) 0.3

Square Roots

✎ Find the value each square root.

1) $\sqrt{25}$

2) $\sqrt{1,600}$

3) $\sqrt{100}$

4) $\sqrt{121}$

5) $\sqrt{4}$

6) $\sqrt{225}$

7) $\sqrt{10,000}$

8) $\sqrt{16}$

9) $\sqrt{64}$

10) $\sqrt{36}$

11) $\sqrt{484}$

12) $\sqrt{49}$

13) $\sqrt{0.01}$

14) $\sqrt{81}$

15) $\sqrt{961}$

16) $\sqrt{400}$

17) $\sqrt{1}$

18) $\sqrt{196}$

19) $\sqrt{144}$

20) $\sqrt{169}$

21) $\sqrt{676}$

Answers of Worksheets – Chapter 4

Multiplication Property of Exponents

1) 4^5

2) 2^6

3) 2^5

4) $8x^3$

5) $15x^8$

6) $3x^4$

7) $10x^9$

8) $15x^4y^2$

9) $48xy^7$

10) $20x^4y^5$

11) $4x^6$

12) $6x^6y^3$

13) $60x^6y^5$

14) x^9

15) $27x^6$

16) $4x^4y^7$

Division Property of Exponents

1) 4^2

2) $\frac{1}{51^{13}}$

3) $\frac{1}{5}$

4) 3^3

5) $\frac{1}{x^6}$

6) 7

7) $\frac{1}{4x^2}$

8) $9x^2$

9) $\frac{3}{4x}$

10) $\frac{7}{x}$

11) $\frac{3}{7x^3}$

12) $\frac{2}{3x^4}$

13) $\frac{9}{5x^2}$

14) $\frac{2x}{y^5}$

15) $\frac{2y^4}{x^4}$

16) $\frac{2x}{5}$

17) $\frac{8y}{x}$

18) $\frac{3}{7xy^4}$

19) $\frac{1}{5}$

20) $\frac{3}{2x}$

21) $\frac{1}{3}$

Powers of Products and Quotients

1) $8x^6$

2) x^2y^2

3) $25x^6$

4) $81x^6$

5) $16x^4y^6$

6) $25x^4y^6$

7) $8x^3y^6$

8) $8x^{12}y^4$

9) $49x^8y^{16}$

10) $1,000x^3$

11) x^{15}

12) $512x^{30}y^6$

13) $81x^8$

14) $256x^6$

15) $121x^{18}y^6$

16) $36x^{10}y^6$

17) $243x^{15}$

18) $49x^6$

19) $64x^2y^8$ 20) $216x^3y^3$ 21) $225x^4y^6$

Zero and Negative Exponents

1) $\dfrac{1}{16}$

2) $\dfrac{1}{25}$

3) $\dfrac{1}{36}$

4) $\dfrac{1}{81}$

5) $\dfrac{1}{10}$

6) $\dfrac{1}{33}$

7) $\dfrac{1}{6}$

8) $\dfrac{1}{9}$

9) $\dfrac{1}{81}$

10) $\dfrac{1}{4}$

11) $\dfrac{1}{125}$

12) $\dfrac{1}{32}$

13) $\dfrac{1}{121}$

14) $\dfrac{1}{16}$

15) $\dfrac{1}{49}$

16) $\dfrac{1}{8}$

17) $\dfrac{1}{4}$

18) $\dfrac{1}{9}$

19) $\dfrac{1}{64}$

20) $\dfrac{1}{10,000}$

21) $\dfrac{9}{4}$

22) 9

23) 8

24) $\dfrac{25}{36}$

25) $\dfrac{1}{121}$

26) $\dfrac{1}{3}$

Negative Exponents and Negative Bases

1) $\dfrac{1}{7}$

2) $\dfrac{2}{x^2}$

3) x^5

4) $-\dfrac{b^1}{a^2}$

5) $7x^5$

6) $-2\dfrac{bc^2}{5}$

7) $\dfrac{p^2}{6n}$

8) $\dfrac{8c^2}{3b^4}$

9) $\dfrac{89x}{y^2}$

10) 9

11) $\dfrac{49}{36}$

12) $\dfrac{16y^2z^2}{x^2}$

Writing Scientific Notation

1) 2.5×10^4

2) 1.2×10^1

3) 1.5×10^{-3}

4) 5.4×10^4

5) 5.1×10^{-3}

6) 6.66×10^2

7) 7.6×10^{-3}

8) 2.9×10^3

9) 1×10^5

10) 3.6×10^6

11) 6×10^7

12) 1.5×10^2

13) 1.08×10^{-1}

14) 2×10^1

15) 2.6×10^2

16) 1×10^6 17) 1.5×10^{-4} 18) 3×10^{-1}

Square Roots

1) 5	8) 4	15) 31
2) 40	9) 8	16) 20
3) 10	10) 6	17) 1
4) 11	11) 22	18) 14
5) 2	12) 7	19) 12
6) 15	13) 0.1	20) 13
7) 100	14) 9	21) 26

Chapter 5: Algebraic Expressions

Topics that you'll learn in this chapter:

- ➤ Expressions and Variables

- ➤ Simplifying Variable and Polynomial Expressions

- ➤ Translate Phrases into an Algebraic Statement

- ➤ The Distributive Property

- ➤ Evaluating One and two Variable

- ➤ Combining like Terms

"Without mathematics, there's nothing you can do. Everything around you are mathematics. Everything around you are numbers." – *Shakuntala Devi*

Translate Phrases into an Algebraic Statement

✍ Write an algebraic expression for each phrase.

1) fifteen subtracted from a number.

2) The quotient of seventeen and a number.

3) A number increased by fifty.

4) A number divided by -21.

5) The difference between sixty –three and a number.

6) Threefold a number decreased by 45.

7) seven times the sum of a number and -21.

8) The quotient of 90 and the product of a number and -8.

The Distributive Property

✍ Use the distributive property to simply each expression.

1) $4(9 - 3x)$

2) $-(-8 - 4x)$

3) $(-5x - 1)(-2)$

4) $(-3)(2x - 4)$

5) $4(5 + 3x)$

6) $(-9x + 10)3$

7) $(-4 - 5x)(-3)$

8) $(-15)(2x + 3)$

9) $(-2)(3x - 1) + 4(3x + 2)$

10) $(-2x)(-3 + 2x) - 3x(1 - 5x)$

11) $2(-6x - 3) + 5(1 - 2x)$

12) $(-3)(x + 4) - (5 + 2x)$

Evaluating One Variable

🖎 Simplify each algebraic expression.

1) $5x + 4, x = 1$

2) $x + (-4), x = -6$

3) $-10x + 8, x = -2$

4) $\left(-\frac{36}{x}\right) - 10 + 2x, x = 6$

5) $\frac{36}{x} - 3, x = 3$

6) $(-10) - \frac{x}{4} + 4x, x = -8$

7) $15 + 6x - 3, x = -1$

8) $(-5) + \frac{x}{8}, x = 64$

9) $\left(-\frac{24}{x}\right) - 10 + 5x, x = 4$

10) $(-4) + \frac{4x}{9}, x = 81$

Evaluating Two Variables

🖎 Simplify each algebraic expression.

1) $5a - (5 - b),$

$\quad a = 2, b = 3$

2) $5x + 3y - 6 + 3y,$

$\quad x = 3, y = 1$

3) $\left(-\frac{27}{x}\right) + 4 + 3y,$

$\quad x = 3, y = 5$

4) $(-4)(-3a - 5b),$

$\quad a = 3, b = 4$

5) $7x + 10 - 5y,$

$\quad x = 3, y = 6$

6) $18 + 3(-x - 4y),$

$\quad x = 2, y = 5$

7) $12x + 2y,$

$\quad x = 5, y = 10$

8) $x \times 6 \div 3y,$

$\quad x = 6, y = 1$

Expressions and Variables

✍ **Simplify each expression.**

1) $10(-3 - 8x), x = 4$

2) $-3(5 - 8x) - 6x, x = 1$

3) $2x - 8x, x = 2$

4) $x + 12x, x = 6$

5) $20 - 5x + 10x + 5, x = 3$

6) $15(5x + 3), x = 0$

7) $20(4 - x) - 9, x = 2$

8) $20x - 8x - 10, x = 5$

9) $6x + 9y, \ x = 4, y = 2$

10) $6x - 2x, x = 8,$

11) $7(-3x + 11) + 9, x = 7,$

12) $12x - 20x + 25, x = 2,$

13) $6x - 5x - 9, x = 9$

14) $(-3)(-x - 6y), x = 5, y = 2$

15) $18x + 3 - 16\,y, x = 3, y = 5$

16) $(-10)(-5x - 7y), x = 5, y = 5$

Combining like Terms

✍ Simplify each expression.

1) $-8(-5x + 1)$

2) $6(-2 + 4x)$

3) $-8 - 14x + 16x + 3$

4) $9x - 7x - 15 + 18$

5) $(-9)(12x - 21) + 31$

6) $2(4x + 9) + 12x$

7) $4(-2x - 17) + 14(3x + 1)$

8) $(9x - 5y)7 + 25y$

9) $4.5x^3 \times (-8x)$

10) $-19 - 15x^2 + 12x^2$

11) $8 + 15x^2 + 12$

12) $15(-2x - 1) + 28$

13) $9x^2 + 4x + 3x^2$

14) $14x^2 - 11x^2 + 10x$

15) $4x^2 - 8x - 11x$

16) $(-8)(15x - 10)$

17) $9x + 6(3 - 5x)$

18) $-12x + 5(20x - 8)$

19) $6(11x + 0.5)$

20) $-30(x + 1) + 20x$

21) $5x - 16y + 6x + 13y - 23x$

22) $5(-2x + 5y) + 20x - 18y$

23) $(-5x) - 2 + 5x + 3$

24) $11(2x + 1) + 13(x - 1)$

Simplifying Polynomial Expressions

✎ **Simplify each polynomial.**

1) $(2x^2 + 4) - (9 + 5x^2)$

2) $(25x^3 - 12x^2) - (6x^2 - 9x^3)$

3) $14x^5 - 15x^6 + 2x^5 - 16x^6 + x^6$

4) $(-2x^5 + 20 - 4x) + (9x^4 + 10x + 6x^5)$

5) $13x^2 - 15x^4 + 12x^3 + 20x^4 + 13x^3$

6) $-6x^2 + 15x^2 + 17x^3 + 16 - 32$

7) $15x^3 + 12 + 2x^2 - 5x - 10x$

8) $24x^2 - 16x^3 - 4x(2x^2 + 3x)$

9) $(21x^4 - 10x) - (2x - x^4)$

10) $(15x^3 + 20x^4) - (12x^4 - 3x^3)$

11) $(15 + 12x^3) + (3x^3 + 5)$

12) $(7x^2 - 9) + (x^2 - 8x^3)$

Answers of Worksheets – Chapter 5

Translate Phrases into an Algebraic Statement

1) $x - 15$

2) $\frac{17}{x}$

3) $x + 50$

4) $-\frac{x}{21}$

5) $63 - x$

6) $3x - 45$

7) $7(x + (-21))$

8) $-\frac{90}{8x}$

The Distributive Property

1) $-12x + 36$

2) $4x + 8$

3) $10x + 2$

4) $-6x + 12$

5) $12x + 20$

6) $-27x + 30$

7) $15x + 12$

8) $-30x - 45$

9) $6x + 10$

10) $11x^2 + 3x$

11) $-22x - 1$

12) $-5x - 17$

Evaluating One Variable

1) 9

2) -10

3) 28

4) -4

5) 9

6) -40

7) 6

8) 3

9) 4

10) 32

Evaluating Two Variables

1) 8

2) 15

3) 10

4) 116

5) 1

6) -48

7) 80

8) 12

Expressions and Variables

1) -350

2) 3

3) -12

4) 78

5) 40

6) 45

7) 31

8) 50

9) 42

10) 32

11) -61

12) 9

13) 0

14) 51

15) -23

16) 600

Combining like Terms

1) $40x - 8$

2) $24x - 12$

3) $2x - 5$

4) $2x + 3$

5) $220 - 108x$

6) $20x + 18$

7) $34x - 54$

8) $63x - 10y$

9) $-36x^4$

10) $-3x^2 - 19$

11) $15x^2 + 20$

12) $-30x + 13$

13) $12x^2 + 4x$

14) $3x^2 + 10x$

15) $4x^2 - 19x$

16) $-120x + 80$

17) $-21x + 18$

18) $88x - 40$

19) $66x + 3$

20) $-10x - 30$

21) $-12x - 3y$

22) $10x + 7y$

23) 1

24) $35x - 2$

Simplifying Polynomial Expressions

1) $-3x^2 - 5$

2) $34x^3 - 18x^2$

3) $-30x^6 + 16x^5$

4) $4x^5 + 9x^4 + 6x + 20$

5) $5x^4 + 25x^3 + 13x^2$

6) $17x^3 + 9x^2 - 16$

7) $15x^3 + 2x^2 - 15x + 12$

8) $-24x^3 + 12x^2$

9) $22x^4 - 12x$

10) $8x^4 + 18x^3$

11) $15x^3 + 20$

12) $-8x^3 + 8x^2 - 9$

Chapter 6: Equations and Inequalities

Topics that you'll learn in this chapter:

- ➢ One, Two, and Multi – Step Equations

- ➢ Graphing Single– Variable Inequalities

- ➢ One, Two, and Multi – Step Inequalities

- ➢ Solving Systems of Equations by Substitution and Elimination

- ➢ Finding Slope and Writing Linear Equations

- ➢ Graphing Lines Using Slope– Intercept and Standard Form

- ➢ Graphing Linear Inequalities

- ➢ Finding Midpoint and Distance of Two Points

"The study of mathematics, like the Nile, begins in minuteness but ends in magnificence." – Charles Caleb Colton

One–Step Equations

Solve each equation.

1) $x + 4 = 16$

2) $48 = (-2) + x$

3) $5x = (-105)$

4) $(-8) = (8x)$

5) $(-2) = 14 + x$

6) $5 + x = 6$

7) $2x + 3 = (-7)$

8) $28 = x + 7$

9) $(-15) + x = (-15)$

10) $12x = (-36)$

11) $x + 8 = (-27)$

12) $x - 4 = (-44)$

13) $(-20) = x - 45$

14) $(-8x) = 88$

15) $(-16) = (2x)$

16) $x + 13 = 55$

17) $25x = 100$

18) $64 = (-8x)$

19) $12x = 48$

20) $15x = 120$

Two–Step Equations

✏️ **Solve each equation.**

1) $4(2 + 2x) = 8$

2) $(-5)(x - 3) = 25$

3) $(-5)(2x - 5) = (-15)$

4) $4(9 + 3x) = -12$

5) $6(2x + 1) = 30$

6) $2(x + 2) = 42$

7) $2(12 + 6x) = 60$

8) $(-10)(5x) = 100$

9) $4(3x + 3) = 24$

10) $\frac{x - 5}{3} = 4$

11) $18 = \frac{x + 6}{2}$

12) $88 = (-4)(x - 5)$

13) $\frac{2x}{3} - 10 = 2$

14) $-18 = 7 + \frac{x}{4}$

15) $\frac{4 + 2x}{12} = 3$

16) $(-6 + 12x) = 90$

17) $(-2x) + 15 = 45$

18) $\frac{x + 3}{12} = 6$

19) $\frac{3x + 9}{4} = (-9)$

20) $(-4) + \frac{2x}{7} = 16$

Multi–Step Equations

✏️ **Solve each equation.**

1) $8 - 2x = 28$

2) $-10 = -(x + 7)$

3) $2x - 17 = (-x) + 1$

4) $-2x = (-3x) - 8$

5) $5(14 + 2x) + 3x = -x$

6) $x - 11 = x - 5 + 2x$

7) $15 + 2x = (-25) - 2x + 3x$

8) $-3(x - 3x) = 40 - 4x$

9) $24 + 8x + x = (-x + 4)$

10) $-8(1 + 5x) = 152$

11) $16 = (-3x) - 1 + 2$

12) $15 = 2x - 4x + 3$

13) $2(x + 5x) = 144$

14) $-9 = (-x + 1) - 9x$

15) $x + 6 = (-x + 5x)$

16) $4x - 5x = 4x + 15$

17) $5 + x = -(x - 5)$

18) $-7 = (2 + 3x)$

19) $22 + x = -3(2 + x)$

20) $x + 2 = x - 2x + 8$

Graphing Single–Variable Inequalities

 Draw a graph for each inequality.

1) $2 \geq x$

2) $x < 3$

3) $5 \geq x$

4) $x \geq -2$

5) $x > 0$

6) $-1.5 < x$

One–Step Inequalities

Solve each inequality and graph it.

1) $2x + 3 \geq 7$

2) $x - 3 \leq 2$

3) $-2x + 3 \geq -1$

4) $x - 3 > -8$

5) $-3x \geq 12$

6) $5x - 1 < 9$

7) $x + 3 > -3$

Two–Step Inequalities

✎ Solve each inequality and graph it.

1) $x - 4 \leq 4$

2) $x + 4 \geq 5$

3) $3x - 2 \leq 7$

4) $5x + 2 < 12$

5) $x + 7 \geq 9$

6) $3x - 3 \leq 3$

7) $7x - 4 < 3$

8) $8 + x \leq 13$

9) $2x + 7 \leq 11$

10) $10x - 16 < 4$

11) $6x - 11 \geq 1$

12) $2x + 3 < 15$

13) $6x + 4 \geq 28$

14) $11 + 2x < 21$

15) $8 + 2x \geq 28$

16) $9 + 4x < 25$

Multi–Step Inequalities

✎ Solve each inequality.

1) $-(x + 3) + 8 < 25$

2) $\frac{3x + 1}{2} \leq 5$

3) $\frac{x - 4}{3} > 7$

4) $4(x - 2) \leq 8$

5) $\frac{x}{3} + \frac{1}{3} < 2$

6) $\frac{x + 4}{5} > 3$

Solving Systems of Equations by Substitution

✍ Solve each system of equation by substitution.

1) $-x + 5y = -4$

   $x - 3y = 8$

2) $2x + 3y = -6$

   $-2x - y = 8$

3) $x + 2y = -5$

   $5x - 10y = 5$

4) $y = -x + 5$

   $3x - y = -3$

5) $3x = 6$

   $10y = 4x + 2$

6) $3x + 2y = 2$

   $x + 4y = -6$

7) $4x + y = 3$

   $2x + 4y = -2$

8) $4y = 2x + 3$

   $x - 4y = -2$

Solving Systems of Equations by Elimination

✍ Solve each system of equation by elimination.

1) $-5x + y = -5$

$$-y = -6x + 6$$

2) $-6x - 2y = -2$

$$2x - 3y = 8$$

3) $5x - 4y = 8$

$$-6x + y = -21$$

4) $10x - 4y = -24$

$$-x - 20y = -18$$

5) $25x + 3y = -13$

$$12x - 6y = -36$$

6) $x - 8y = -7$

$$6x + 4y = 10$$

7) $-6x + 16y = 4$

$$5x + y = 11$$

8) $2x - 3y = -10$

$$4x + 6y = -20$$

Systems of Equations Word Problems

✍ Solve.

1) A school of 220 students went on a field trip. They took 20 vehicles, some vans and some minibuses. Find the number of vans and the number of minibuses they took if each van holds 5 students and each minibus hold 15 students.

2) The sum of two numbers is 28. Their difference is 12. Find the numbers.

3) A farmhouse shelters 20 animals, some are pigs, and some are gooses. Altogether there are 64 legs. How many of each animal are there?

4) The sum of the digits of a certain two–digit number is 15. Reversing it's increasing the number by 9. What is the number?

5) The difference of two numbers is 16. Their sum is 32. Find the numbers.

Linear Equations

✏️ **Find the slope of the line through each pair of points.**

1) $(3,1),(2,4)$

2) $(-3,4),(-1,6)$

3) $(4, 4),(6,-6)$

4) $(-1,8),(5,-4)$

5) $(12,-3),(7,-3)$

6) $(11,-14),(13,-4)$

7) $(-4,6),(-10, 0)$

8) $(10,12),(2,-4)$

9) $(12,-1),(0,5)$

10) $(-1,7),(-2,2)$

11) $(11,12),(1,22)$

12) $(36,9),(6,-11)$

✏️ **Write the slope–intercept form of the equation of the line through the given**

points.

1) Through: $(2,3),(4,2)$

2) Through: $(8,-3),(6,7)$

3) Through: $(0.5,4),(2.5,4.4)$

4) Through: $(4,-2),(2.5,1)$

5) Through: $(-1,0.7),(-2.3,2)$

6) Through: $(4,7),(2,10)$

7) Through: $(2.7,6),(4.5,6)$

8) Through: $(-3,2),(1,6)$

9) Through: $(1,-2),(8,12)$

10) Through: $(1.5,6),(-2.5,2)$

11) Through: $(2,0),(-3,-2)$

12) Through: $(9,4),(1,-4)$

Graphing Lines of Equations

📝 Sketch the graph of each line

1) $y = 3x - 2$

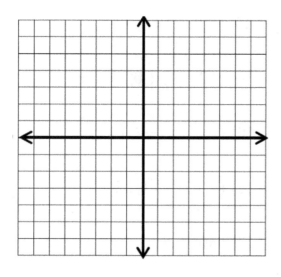

2) $y = 2x + 3$

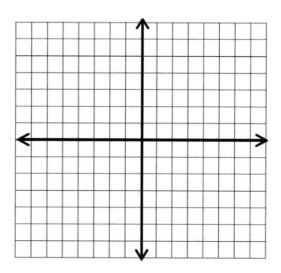

3) $-2x = y + 5$

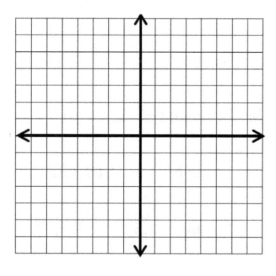

4) $4x + y = 2$

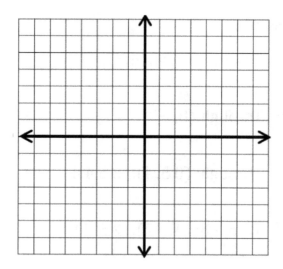

Graphing Linear Inequalities

✏️ Sketch the graph of each linear inequality.

1) $2y + 8x \geq 4$

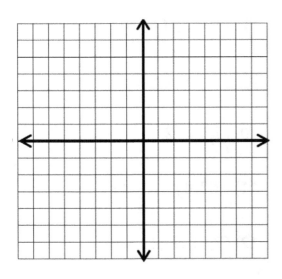

2) $-x + 2y \leq 4$

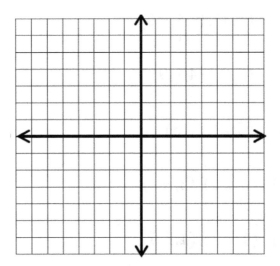

3) $2x + \frac{1}{2}y < 2$

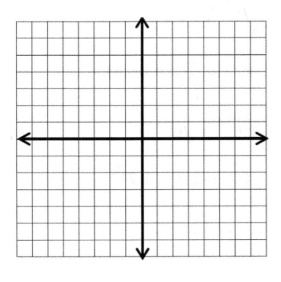

4) $-\frac{1}{3}x + y < 2$

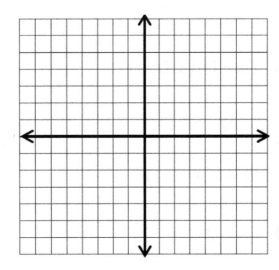

Finding Distance of Two Points

✎ Find the midpoint of the line segment with the given endpoints.

1) $(1.5, -1), (0.5, -1)$

2) $(4, 1), (-1, -5)$

3) $(0, 3), (4, -9)$

4) $(5, 2), (1, 5)$

5) $(-2, 0), (3, -4)$

6) $(1, -2), (1.5, 5)$

7) $(1.25, 2.5), (-0.25, -1.5)$

8) $(1, 0.5), (-2, 0.5)$

9) $(-3, 6), (-1, -2)$

10) $(1, 7), (2, 1)$

11) $(3.2, 4), (1, -4)$

12) $(7, 8), (3, 2)$

✎ Find the distance between each pair of points.

1) $(3, 4), (2, -1)$

2) $(6, -1), (2, 3)$

3) $(2, 5), (-2, 5)$

4) $(0, -4), (-5, 1)$

5) $(3, -2), (-1, -5)$

6) $(10, 4), (-1, -7)$

7) $(2, 5), (2, 4)$

8) $(5, 8), (-3, -4)$

9) $(8, 3), (9, -6)$

10) $(-2, 3), (4, 7)$

11) $(8, 5), (-1, 0)$

12) $(4, -1), (0, 1)$

Answers of Worksheets – Chapter 6

One–Step Equations

1) 12	6) 1	11) − 35	16) 42
2) 50	7) − 5	12) − 40	17) 4
3) − 21	8) 21	13) −25	18) − 8
4) −1	9) 0	14) -11	19) 4
5) − 16	10) − 3	15) -8	20) 8

Two–Step Equations

1) 0	6) 10	11) 30	16) 8
2) -2	7) 3	12) − 17	17) -15
3) 4	8) -2	13) 18	18) 69
4) -4	9) 1	14) -100	19) − 15
5) 2	10) 17	15) 16	20) 70

Multi–Step Equations

1) −10	8) 4	15) 2
2) 3	9) −2	16) -3
3) 6	10) − 4	17) 0
4) −8	11) − 5	18) − 3
5) − 5	12) −6	19) − 7
6) −3	13) 12	20) 3
7) −40	14) 1	

Graphing Single–Variable Inequalities

1) $2 \geq x$

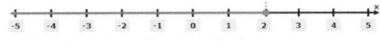

2) $x < 3$

3) $5 \geq x$

4) $x \geq -2$

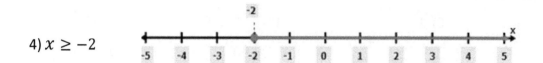

5) $x > 0$

6) $-1.5 < x$

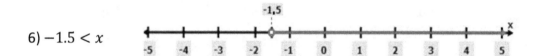

One–Step Inequalities

1)

2)

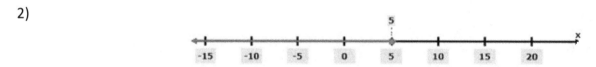

3)

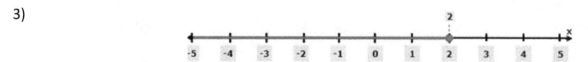

4)

5)

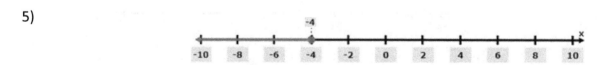

6)

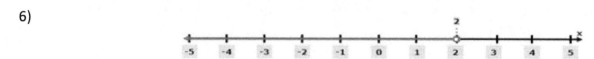

7)

Two–Step inequalities

1) $x \leq 8$

2) $x \geq 1$

3) $x \leq 3$

4) $x < 2$

5) $x \geq 2$

6) $x \leq 2$

7) $x < 1$

8) $x \leq 5$

9) $x \leq 2$

10) $x < 2$

11) $x \geq 2$

12) $x < 6$

13) $x \geq 4$

14) $x < 5$

15) $x \geq 10$

16) $x < 4$

Multi–Step inequalities.

1) $x > -20$

2) $x \leq 3$

3) $x > 25$

4) $x \leq 4$

5) $x < 5$

$x > 11$

Solving Systems of Equations by Substitution

1) $(14, 2)$

2) $(-\frac{9}{2}, 1)$

3) $(-2, -\frac{3}{2})$

4) $(\frac{1}{2}, \frac{9}{2})$

5) $(2, 1)$

6) $(2, -2)$

7) $(1, -1)$

8) $(-1, \frac{1}{4})$

Solving Systems of Equations by Elimination

1) $(1, 0)$

2) $(1, -2)$

3) $(4, 3)$

4) $(-2, 1)$

5) $(-1, 4)$

6) $(1, 1)$

7) $(2, 1)$

8) $(-5, 0)$

Systems of Equations Word Problems

1) There are 8 van and 12 minibuses.

2) 8 and 20

3) There are 12 pigs and 8 gooses.

4) 78

5) 24 and 8.

Finding Slope

1) -3

2) 1

3) -5

4) -2

5) 0

6) 5

7) 1

8) 2

9) $-\frac{1}{2}$ 10) 5 11) -1 12) $\frac{2}{3}$

Writing Linear Equations

1) $y = -\frac{1}{2}x + 4$

2) $y = -5x + 37$

3) $y = \frac{1}{5}x + \frac{39}{10}$

4) $y = -2x + 6$

5) $y = -x - 0.3$

6) $y = -\frac{3}{2}x + 13$

7) $y = 6$

8) $y = x + 5$

9) $y = 2x - 4$

10) $y = x + 4.5$

11) $y = \frac{2}{5}x - \frac{4}{5}$

12) $y = x - 5$

Graphing Lines Using Slope–Intercept Form

1)

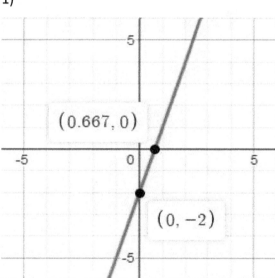

$(0.667, 0)$

$(0, -2)$

2)

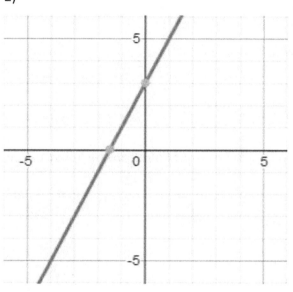

3)

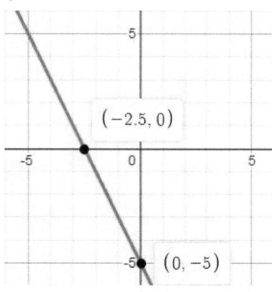

$(-2.5, 0)$

$(0, -5)$

4)

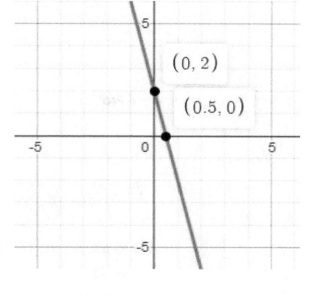

$(0, 2)$

$(0.5, 0)$

Graphing Linear Inequalities

1)

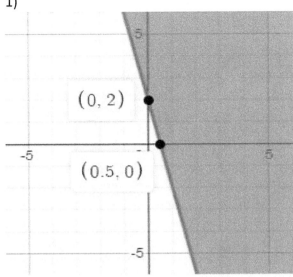

2)

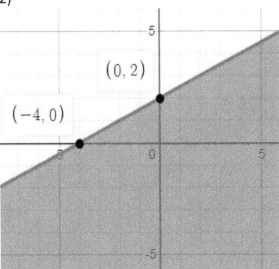

3)

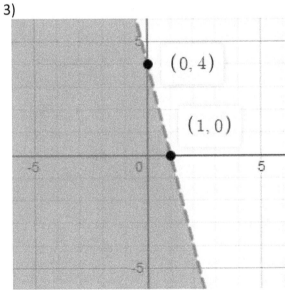

4)

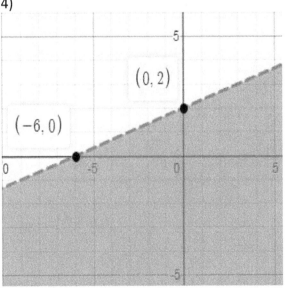

Finding Midpoint

1) $(1, -1)$	4) $(3, 3.5)$	7) $(0.5, 0.5)$	10) $(1.5, 4)$
2) $(1.5, -2)$	5) $(0.5, -2)$	8) $(-0.5, 0.5)$	11) $(2.1, 0)$
3) $(2, -3)$	6) $(1.25, 1.5)$	9) $(-2, 2)$	12) $(5, 5)$

Finding Distance of Two Points

1) 5.09	4) 7.07	7) 1	10) 7.21
2) 5.656	5) 5	8) 14.42	11) 10.29
3) 4	6) 15.56	9) 9.055	12) 4.47

Chapter 7: Polynomials

Topics that you'll learn in this chapter:

- ➤ Classifying Polynomials
- ➤ Writing Polynomials in Standard Form
- ➤ Simplifying Polynomials
- ➤ Adding and Subtracting Polynomials
- ➤ Multiplying and Dividing Monomials
- ➤ Multiplying a Polynomial and a Monomial
- ➤ Multiplying Binomials
- ➤ Factoring Trinomials
- ➤ Operations with Polynomials

"Mathematics – the unshaken Foundation of Sciences, and the plentiful Fountain of Advantage to human affairs." – Isaac Barrow

Classifying Polynomials

✍ Name each polynomial by degree and number of terms.

1) -5

2) $x + 1$

3) $3x - 2$

4) $8x^6 - 7$

5) $3x^2 - x$

6) $5x^2 - 6x^3$

7) $-10x^4$

8) $17x^5$

9) $-10 + 4x^2 + 2x$

10) $11x^6 - 9$

11) $7x^6 + 5x^2 - 4x^4$

12) $-8x^4 + 3x^3 - 2x^2 - 3x$

13) $2x - 12x^2 + 5x^3 - 4x^4$

14) $12x^6 + 7x^5 - 3x^2$

✍ Write each polynomial in standard form

1) $12x^4 + x - 4x^3$

2) $x + x^3 - 9$

3) $12 - x^3 - 3x^5 + 9x^4$

4) $x^2 + 12 - x$

5) $x(x + 2) - (3x^5 + 2)$

6) $x^2 + 13x^5 + x^3 - 4x$

7) $10 + x^3 + x^3 - 3x^5 + 2x^3$

8) $x(x + x^5 + x^3 + 6)$

9) $x^5 + 2x^3(x^2 + 2)$

10) $x + (x + 2)$

11) $x^4 + 2x^5 + x^3$

12) $(x - 5)(x + 5)$

13) $x(1 + 2x^3 + 2x)$

14) $2 - 8x + 2x^2$

Simplifying Polynomials

✏️ Simplify each expression.

1) $-3x^2 + x^5 + 7x^5 - 2x^2 + 6$

2) $18x^5 - 3x^5 + 7x^2 - 15x^5 + 4$

3) $x(x^3 + 9) - 6(8 + x^2)$

4) $x(x^2 + 2x^3) - x^3 + x$

5) $4 - 17x^2 + 30x^2 - 17x^2 + 26$

6) $4x^2 - 8x + 3x^3 + 15x - 20x$

7) $(x - 6)(x - x^2 + 5)$

8) $(x - 5)(x + 5)$

9) $(7x^3 + 28x^2 + 28x) \div 7(2x + x^2)$

10) $(12x + 9x^2 + 4) \div (3x + 2)$

11) $(x^4 - x) + (4x^2 - 3x^4)$

12) $x(x^2 + x + 3)$

13) $(4x + 5)(4x - 5)$

14) $(x^2 - 3x) + (12 + 8x^2 + 18x)$

Adding and Subtracting Polynomials

✎ **Simplify each expression.**

1) $(x^3 + 6) - (6 + 3x^3)$

2) $(x^2 + 8) + (7x^2 - 8)$

3) $(2x^2 + x^3) - (5x^2 + 1)$

4) $(6x^2 - 4x) + (3x - 6x^2 + 1)$

5) $(x - 2x^3) - (4x^3 + 4)$

6) $(2x^3 + 2x^2) - (2x^2 - x^3 + 2)$

7) $(4x^2 - 3) + (x^2 - x^3)$

8) $(x^3 + 13x^4) - (13x^4 + 3x^3)$

9) $(-x^4 + 2x^5 + 3x^3) + (14x^3 + 16x^4)$

10) $(10x^3 - 6x^6 - x + 5) + (-10x^3 + 11x^6 - 9x)$

11) $(42 + 8x^4 - 4x^2) + (2x^4 + 2x^2) - (22 - 5x^4)$

12) $(-3x^3 - 3x + 2) + (3x + 8x^4 - 10) + (x^2 + x^3 + 10)$

Multiplying Monomials

✎ **Simplify each expression.**

1) $2xy^2 \times 3z^2$

2) $3xyz \times 5x^2y$

3) $4pq^3 \times (-3p^3q)$

4) $s^3t^2 \times 2st^5$

5) $5p^3 \times (-2p^2)$

6) $-2p^2r \times 6pr^3$

7) $(-a)(-4a^6b)$

8) $2u^2v^3 \times (-8u^3v^3)$

9) $6u^3 \times (2u)$

10) $-5y^2 \times 4x^2y$

11) $13y^2z^2 \times (-y^4z)$

12) $8a^3c^2 \times 5abc^2$

Multiply and Divide Monomials

🖋 Simplify.

1) $(x^3y^2)(42y^4)$

2) $\dfrac{100x^5y^6}{25x^6y^{11}}$

3) $(8x^4)(12x^5)$

4) $\dfrac{75x^{16}y^{10}}{5x^6y^7}$

5) $(-2x^{-3}y^2)^2$

6) $\dfrac{15x^{12}y^5}{5x^9y^2}$

7) $(11x^2y^4)(4x^9y^{10})$

8) $\dfrac{50x^4y^7}{25x^3y^7}$

9) $(2x^{-3}y^4)^2$

10) $\dfrac{-21x^8y^{13}}{3x^6y^6}$

11) $(2x^{-2}y^{-1})(-4x^{-2}y^3)$

12) $\dfrac{121x^6y^9}{11x^3y^7}$

Multiply a Polynomial and a Monomial

🖋 Find each product.

1) $3(2x - 2y)$

2) $5x(4x - y)$

3) $-2x(x + 5)$

4) $11(3x + 7)$

5) $10x(5x - 2y)$

6) $4(3x - 5y)$

7) $2x(3x^3 - 5x + 4)$

8) $-4x(2 + 4xy)$

9) $3(2x^2 - 8x + 3)$

10) $-3x^2(3x^2 + 5)$

11) $x^2(4x^3 - 2xy + xy^2)$

12) $3x^2(3 - 5x)$

13) $2x^2(x^4 + 5x - 9)$

14) $4x(7x^2 - 5y + y^2)$

Multiply Binomials

✎ Multiply.

1) $(2x - 2)(x + 3)$

2) $(4x + 2)(2x + 1)$

3) $(x + 3)(x + 4)$

4) $(x^2 + 5)(x^2 - 5)$

5) $(2x - 3)(x + 4)$

6) $(2x - 6)(x + 7)$

7) $(x - 2)(3x - 4)$

8) $(2x - 5)(x + 4)$

9) $(x + 10)(x - 10)$

10) $(x - 3)(3x + 4)$

11) $(x - 5)(2x + 8)$

12) $(x - 1)(4x + 2)$

13) $(2x - 1)(2x + 1)$

14) $(x + 5)(x - 3)$

15) $(x + 4)(x + 7)$

16) $(x + 2)(4x - 1)$

Factor Trinomials

✎ Factor each trinomial.

1) $x^2 - 12x + 27$

2) $x^2 + 5x - 24$

3) $x^2 + 13x + 30$

4) $x^2 - 81$

5) $2x^2 + 12x - 14$

6) $x^2 + 2x - 8$

7) $2x^2 + 3x + 1$

8) $2x^2 + 2x - 4$

9) $9x^2 + 3x - 2$

10) $x^2 + 15x + 56$

11) $16x^2 + 12xy + 2y^2$

12) $3x^2 - 14x + 8$

13) $2x^2 - 8x + 8$

14) $5x^2 + 12x + 4$

Operations with Polynomials

✎ **Find each product.**

1) $x^2(3x - 2)$

2) $2x^2(5x - 3)$

3) $-x(5x - 3)$

4) $x^2(-3x + 9)$

5) $5(7x + 3)$

6) $8(3x + 8)$

7) $5(10x + 4)$

8) $-3x^5(x - 3)$

9) $5(3x^2 - x + 2)$

10) $4(x^2 - 2x + 3)$

11) $10(6x^2 + 5x - 2)$

12) $3x(2x^2 + 2x + 7)$

13) $(7x + 1)(x - 2)$

14) $(x + 11)(3x - 1)$

15) $(3x + 2)(3x - 2)$

16) $(2x - 4)(x + 2)$

Answers of Worksheets – Chapter 7

Classifying Polynomials

1) Constant monomial
2) Linear binomial
3) Linear binomial
4) Sixth degree binomial
5) Quadratic binomial
6) cubic binomial
12) Quartic polynomial with four terms
13) Quartic polynomial with four terms
14) Sixth degree trinomial

7) Quartic monomial
8) Quantic binomial
9) Quadratic trinomial
10) Sixth degree binomial
11) Sixth degree trinomial

Writing Polynomials in Standard Form

1) $12x^4 - 4x^3 + x$
2) $x^3 + x - 9$
3) $-3x^5 + 9x^4 - x^3 + 12$
4) $x^2 - x + 12$
5) $-3x^5 + x^2 + 2x - 2$
6) $13x^5 + x^3 + x^2 - 4x$
7) $-3x^5 + 4x^3 + 10$

8) $x^6 + x^4 + x^2 + 6x$
9) $2x^6 + x^5 + 4x^3$
10) $2x + 2$
11) $2x^5 + x^4 + x^3$
12) $x^2 - 25$
13) $2x^4 + 2x^2 + x$
14) $2x^2 - 8x + 2$

Simplifying Polynomials

1) $8x^5 - 5x^2 + 6$
2) $7x^2 + 4$
3) $x^4 - 6x^2 + 9x - 48$

4) $2x^4 + x$
5) $-4x^2 + 30$
6) $3x^3 + 4x^2 - 13x$

7) $-x^3 + 7x^2 - x - 30$

8) $x^2 - 25$

9) $x + 2$

10) $3x + 2$

11) $-2x^4 + 4x^2 - x$

12) $x^3 + x^2 + 3x$

13) $16x^2 - 25$

14) $9x^2 + 15x + 12$

Adding and Subtracting Polynomials

1) $-2x^3$

2) $8x^2$

3) $x^3 - 3x^2 + 1$

4) $-x + 1$

5) $-6x^3 + x - 4$

6) $3x^3 - 2$

7) $-x^3 + 5x^2 - 3$

8) $-2x^3$

9) $2x^5 + 15x^4 + 17x^3$

10) $5x^6 - 10x + 5$

11) $5x^4 - 2x^2 + 20$

12) $8x^4 - 2x^3 + x^2 + 2$

Multiply Monomials

1) $6xy^2z^2$

2) $15x^3y^2z$

3) $-12p^4q^4$

4) $2s^4t^{10}$

5) $-10p^5$

6) $-12p^3r^4$

7) $4a^7b$

8) $-16u^5v^6$

9) $12u^4$

10) $-20x^2y^3$

11) $-13y^6z^3$

12) $40a^4bc^4$

Multiply and Divide Monomials

1) $42x^3y^6$

2) $4x^{-1}y^{-5}$

3) $96x^9$

4) $15x^{10}y^3$

5) $4x^{-6}y^4$

6) $3x^3y^3$

7) $44x^{11}y^{14}$

8) $2x$

9) $4x^{-6}y^8$

10) $-7x^2y^7$

11) $-8x^{-4}y^2$

12) $11x^3y^2$

Multiply a Polynomial and a Monomial

1) $6x - 6y$

2) $20x^2 - 5xy$

3) $-2x^2 - 10$

4) $33x + 77$

5) $50x^2 - 20xy$

6) $12x - 20y$

7) $6x^4 - 10x^2 + 8x$

8) $-16x^2y - 8x$

9) $6x^2 - 24x + 9$

10) $-9x^4 - 15x^2$

11) $4x^5 - 2x^3y + y^2x^3$

12) $9x^2 - 15x^3$

13) $2x^6 + 10x^3 - 18x^2$

14) $28x^3 - 20xy + 4xy^2$

Multiplying Binomials

1) $2x^2 + 4x - 6$

2) $8x^2 + 8x + 2$

3) $x^2 + 7x + 12$

4) $x^4 - 25$

5) $2x^2 + 5x - 12$

6) $2x^2 + 8x - 42$

7) $3x^2 - 10x + 8$

8) $2x^2 + 3x - 20$

9) $x^2 - 100$

10) $3x^2 - 5x - 12$

11) $2x^2 - 2x - 40$

12) $4x^2 - 2x - 2$

13) $4x^2 - 1$

14) $x^2 + 2x - 15$

15) $x^2 + 11x + 28$

16) $4x^2 + 7x - 2$

Factoring Trinomials

1) $(x - 3)(x - 9)$

2) $(x + 8)(x - 3)$

3) $(x + 10)(x + 3)$

4) $(x + 9)(x - 9)$

5) $(x + 7)(2x - 2)$

6) $(x - 2)(x + 4)$

7) $(2x + 1)(x + 1)$

8) $(2x - 2)(x + 2)$

9) $(3x - 1)(3x + 2)$

10) $(x + 7)(x + 8)$

11) $(4x + y)(4x + 2y)$

12) $(x - 4)(3x - 2)$

13) $(2x - 4)(x - 2)$

14) $(x + 2)(5x + 2)$

Operations with Polynomials

1) $3x^3 - 2x^2$

2) $10x^3 - 6x^2$

3) $-5x^2 + 3x$

4) $-3x^3 + 9x^2$

5) $35x + 15$

6) $24x + 64$

7) $50x + 20$

8) $-3x^6 + 9x^5$

9) $15x^2 - 5x + 10$

10) $4x^2 - 8x + 12$

11) $60x^2 + 50x - 20$

12) $6x^3 + 6x^2 + 21x$

13) $7x^2 - 13x - 2$

14) $3x^2 + 32x - 11$

15) $9x^2 - 4$

16) $2x^2 - 8$

Chapter 8: Geometry

Topics that you'll learn in this chapter:

- ➤ The Pythagorean Theorem

- ➤ Area of Triangles and Trapezoids

- ➤ Area and Circumference of Circles

- ➤ Area and Perimeter of Polygons

- ➤ Area of Squares, Rectangles, and Parallelograms

- ➤ Volume of Cubes, Rectangle Prisms, and Cylinder

- ➤ Surface Area of Cubes, Rectangle Prisms, and Cylinder

"Mathematics is, as it were, a sensuous logic, and relates to philosophy as do the arts, music, and plastic art to poetry." — *K. Shegel*

The Pythagorean Theorem

✎ Do the following lengths form a right triangle?

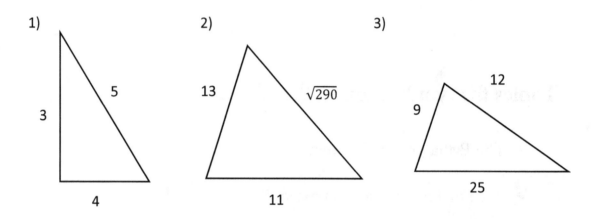

1)

3 5 4

2)

13 √290 11

3)

12 9 25

✎ Find each missing length to the nearest tenth.

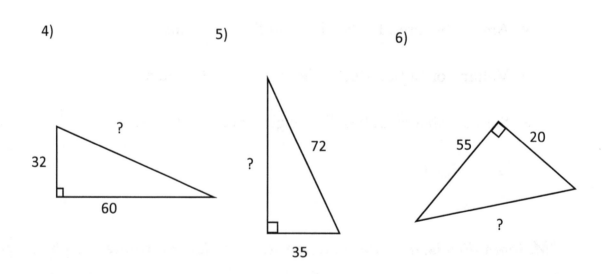

4)

? 32 60

5)

72 ? 35

6)

55 20 ?

Angles

✍ **What is the value of x in the following figures?**

1)
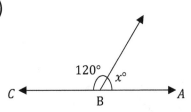

2)
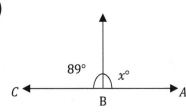

3)
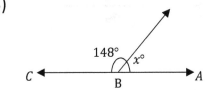

4)
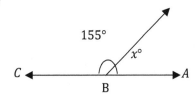

5)
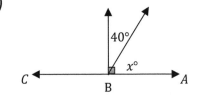

6)
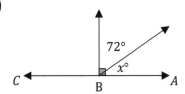

✍ *Solve.*

7) Six supplement peer to each other angles have equal measures. What is the measure of each angle? _____

8) The measure of an angle is one fourth the measure of its complementary. What is the measure of the angle? _____

Area of Triangles

✎ Find the area of each.

1)

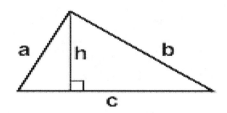

c = 15 mi

h = 4 mi

2)

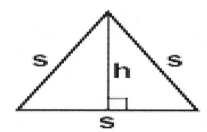

s = 6 m

h = 5.2 m

3)

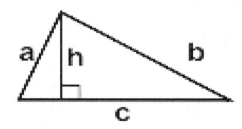

a = 9.5 m

b = 25 m

c = 18 m

h = 9 m

4)

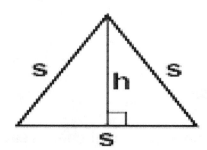

s = 8 m

h = 6.93 m

Area of Trapezoids

✍Calculate the area for each trapezoid.

1)

12 cm

8 cm

15 cm

2)

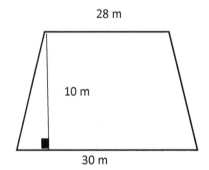

28 m

10 m

30 m

3)

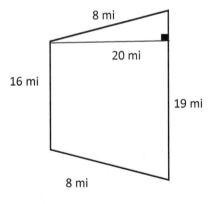

8 mi

20 mi

16 mi

19 mi

8 mi

4)

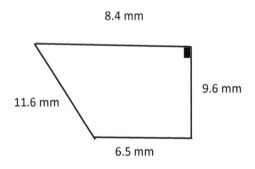

8.4 mm

11.6 mm

9.6 mm

6.5 mm

Area and Perimeter of Polygons

✎ Find the area and perimeter of each

1)

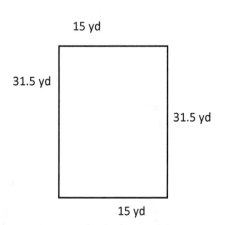

15 yd

31.5 yd

31.5 yd

15 yd

2)

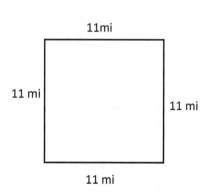

11mi

11 mi

11 mi

11 mi

3)

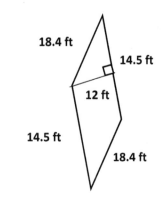

18.4 ft

14.5 ft

12 ft

14.5 ft

18.4 ft

4)

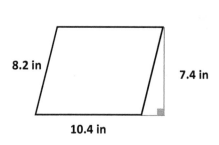

8.2 in

7.4 in

10.4 in

5)

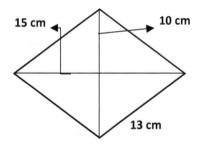

15 cm

10 cm

13 cm

6)

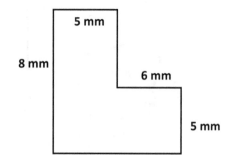

5 mm

8 mm

6 mm

5 mm

✎ **Find the perimeter of each shape.**

7)

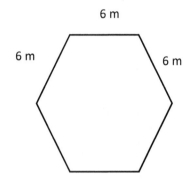

6 m

6 m

6 m

8)

11mm

11 mm

9)

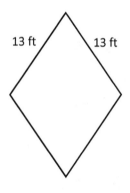

13 ft

13 ft

10)

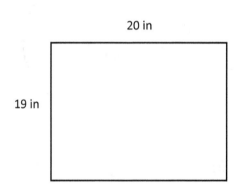

20 in

19 in

11)

8.5 cm

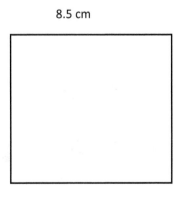

12)

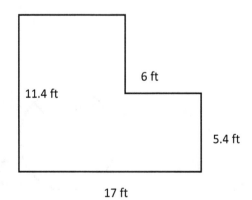

6 ft

11.4 ft

5.4 ft

17 ft

Area and Circumference of Circles

✍ **Find the area and circumference of each.** ($\pi = 3.14$)

1)

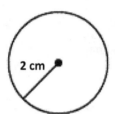

2)

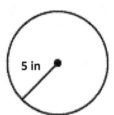

3)

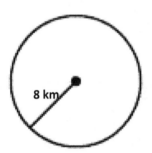

4)

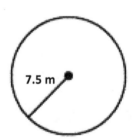

5)

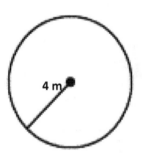

6)

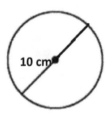

7)

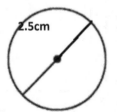

8)

Volume of Cubes

✎ Find the volume of each.

1)

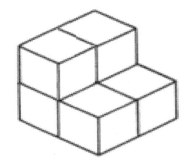

2)

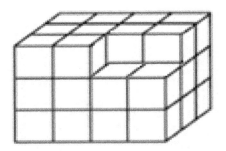

3)

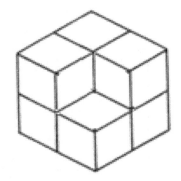

4)

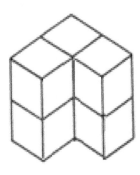

5)

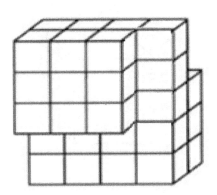

6)

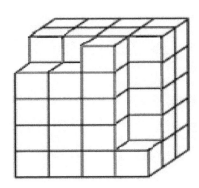

Volume of Rectangle Prisms

✎ Find the volume of each of the rectangular prisms.

1)

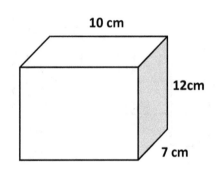

2)

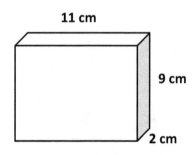

3)

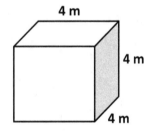

4)

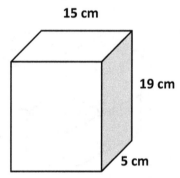

5)

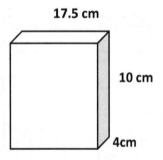

6)

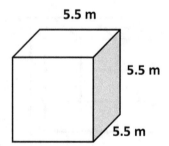

Surface Area of Cubes

✎ Find the surface of each cube.

1)

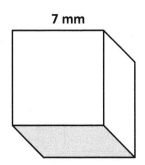

7 mm

2)

10.5 mm

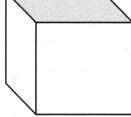

3)

3.5 cm

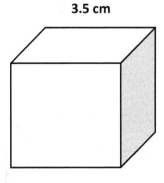

4)

4 m

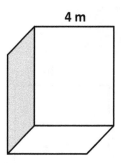

5)

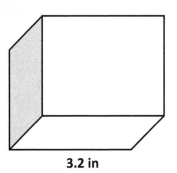

3.2 in

6)

8.1 ft

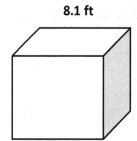

Surface Area of a Rectangle Prism

Find the surface of each prism.

1)

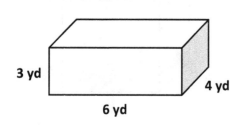

3 yd
4 yd
6 yd

2)

1.02 mm

1.5 mm

0.5 mm

3)

2.5 in

9.5 in

4 in

4)

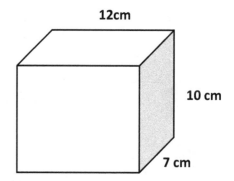

12cm

10 cm

7 cm

Volume of a Cylinder

✎ **Find the volume of each cylinder.** ($\pi = 3.14$)

1)

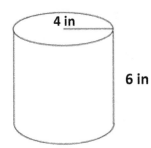

4 in

6 in

2)

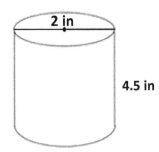

7 m

10 m

3)

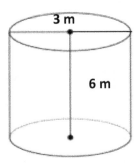

3 m

6 m

4)

2 in

4.5 in

5)

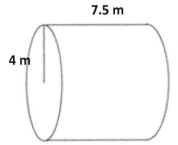

7.5 m

4 m

6)

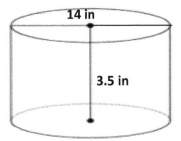

14 in

3.5 in

Surface Area of a Cylinder

Find the surface of each cylinder. ($\pi = 3.14$)

1)

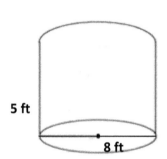

5 ft
8 ft

2)

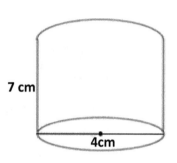

7 cm
4cm

3)

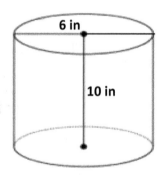

6 in
10 in

4)

2 yd
5.5 yd

5)

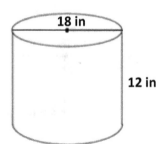

18 in
12 in

6)

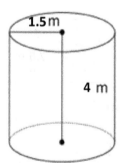

1.5 m
4 m

Answers of Worksheets – Chapter 8

The Pythagorean Theorem

1) yes
2) yes
3) no
4) 68
5) 62.92
6) 58.52

Angles

1) 60°
2) 91°
3) 32°
4) 25°
5) 50°
6) 18°
7) 30°
8) 18°

Area of Triangles

1) 30 mi^2
2) 15.6 m^2
3) 81 m^2
4) 27.72m^2

Area of Trapezoids

1) 108 cm^2
2) 290 m^2
3) 350 mi^2
4) 71.52 mm^2

Area of Squares, Rectangles, and Parallelograms

1) Area: 472.5 m^2, Perimeter: 93m

2) Area: 121 mm^2, Perimeter: 44mm

3) Area: 174 ft^2, Perimeter: 65.8 ft

4) Area: 76.96 in^2, Perimeter: 37.2in

5) Area: 75cm^2, Perimeter 52 cm

6) Area: 70 mm^2, Perimeter:38 mm

7) P: 36 m
8) P: 44 mm
9) P: 52 ft
10) P: 78 in
11) P: 34 cm
12) P: 56.8 ft

Area and Circumference of Circles

1) Area: 12.56 cm^2, Circumference: 12.56 cm.

2) Area: 78.5 in^2, Circumference: 31.4 in.

3) Area: 200.96 km^2, Circumference: 50.24 km.

4) Area: 176.625 m^2, Circumference: 47.1 m.

5) Area: 50.24 m², Circumference: 25.12 m

6) Area: 78.5 cm², Circumference: 31.4 cm.

7) Area: 4.906 cm², Circumference: 7.85 cm.

8) Area: 1.766 in², Circumference: 4.71 in.

Volumes of Cubes

1) 6

2) 34

3) 7

4) 6

5) 41

6) 54

Volume of Rectangle Prisms

1) 840 cm³

2) 198 cm³

3) 64 m³

4) 1,425 cm³

5) 700 cm³

6) 166.375 cm³

Surface Area of a Cube

1) 294 mm²

2) 661.5 mm²

3) 73.5 cm²

4) 96 m²

5) 61.44 in²

6) 393.66 ft²

Surface Area of a Rectangle Prism

1) 108 yd²

2) 5.58 mm²

3) 143.5 in²

4) 548 cm²

Volume of a Cylinder

1) 301.44 cm³

2) 1538.6cm³

3) 42.39 m³

4) 14.13 m³

5) 376.8 m³

6) 538.51 m³

Surface Area of a Cylinder

1) 226.08 ft²

2) 113.04 cm²

3) 224.92 in²

4) 94.2 yd²

5) 1,186.92 in²

6) 51.81m²

Chapter 9: Statistics

Topics that you'll learn in this chapter:

- ➢ Mean, Median, Mode, and Range of the Given Data

- ➢ Box and Whisker Plots

- ➢ Bar Graph

- ➢ Stem– And– Leaf Plot

- ➢ The Pie Graph or Circle Graph

- ➢ Dot and Scatter Plots

- ➢ Probability of Simple Events

"The book of nature is written in the language of Mathematic" -*Galileo*

Mean and Median

✎ **Find Mean and Median of the Given Data.**

1) 8, 10, 7, 3, 12

2) 4, 6, 9, 7, 5, 19

3) 5, 11, 1, 1, 8, 9 , 20

4) 12, 4, 2, 7, 3, 2

5) 3, 5, 7, 4, 7, 8, 9

6) 5, 10, 4, 4, 9, 12, 9

7) 10, 4, 8, 5, 9, 6, 7, 19

8) 16, 3, 4, 3, 7, 6, 18

9) 22, 20, 5, 11, 32, 44, 71

10) 14, 8, 9, 5, 4, 13, 8, 10

11) 8, 15, 35, 66, 41, 21

12) 24, 23, 54, 38, 71, 81

✎ **Solve.**

13) In a javelin throw competition, five athletics score 23, 45,53.53,13and 61 meters. What are their Mean and Median? _____

14) Eva went to shop and bought 7 apples, 4 peaches, 6 bananas, 3 pineapple and 4melons. What are the Mean and Median of her purchase? _____

Mode and Range

✍ **Find Mode and Rage of the Given Data.**

1) 10, 12, 8, 8,4, 1, 9

   Mode: _____Range: _____

2) 4, 6, 4, 13, 2, 13, 19, 13

   Mode: _____Range: _____

3) 8, 8, 7, 2, 7, 7, 5, 6, 5

   Mode: _____Range: _____

4) 12, 9, 12,6, 12, 9, 10

   Mode: _____Range: _____

5) 2, 2, 4, 3, 2, 10, 8

   Mode: _____Range: _____

6) 6, 1, 4, 20, 19, 2, 7, 1, 5, 1

   Mode: _____Range: _____

7) 16,35, 9, 7, 7, 5, 14, 13, 7

   Mode: _____Range: _____

8) 7, 6, 6, 9, 16, 6, 7, 5

   Mode: _____Range: _____

9) 12, 5, 6, 12, 4, 4, 6, 4, 5

   Mode: _____Range: _____

10) 2, 5, 10, 5, 4, 5, 10, 10

   Mode: _____Range: _____

11) 4,11, 5, 3, 12, 12, 18, 2

   Mode: _____Range: _____

12) 6, 3, 3, 9, 6, 16, 3, 10

   Mode: _____Range: _____

✍**Solve.**

13) A stationery sold 15 pencils, 26 red pens, 22 blue pens, 10 notebooks, 12 erasers, 22 rulers and 42 color pencils. What are the Mode and Range for the stationery sells?

   Mode: _____   Range: _____

14)In an English test, eight students score 24, 13, 17, 21, 19, 13, 13 and 17. What are their Mode and Range? _____

Times Series

📖 **Use the following Graph to complete the table.**

Day	Distance (km)
1	
2	

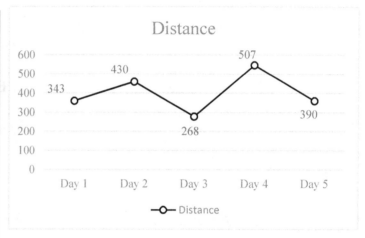

The following table shows the number of births in the US from 2007 to 2012 (in millions).

Year	Number of births (in millions)
2007	6.42
2008	6.45
2009	6.33
2010	5.9
2011	4.35
2012	4.35

Draw a time series for the table.

Box and Whisker Plot

 Make box and whisker plots for the given data.

$1, 5, 20, 8, 3, 10, 13, 11, 14, 17, 18, 15, 23$

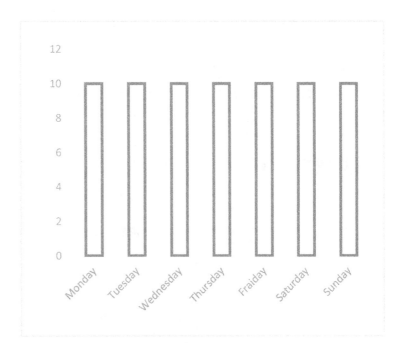

Bar Graph

Graph the given information as a bar graph.

Day	Sale House
Monday	6
Tuesday	4
Wednesday	10
Thursday	5
Friday	2
Saturday	8
Sunday	1

Dot plots

A survey of "How many pets each person owned?" has these results:

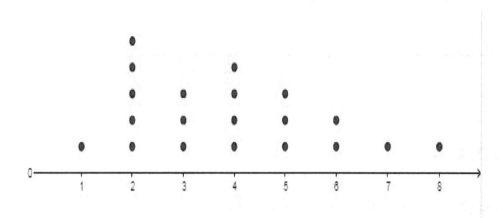

1) How many people have at least 3 pets?

2) How many people have 2 and 3 pets?

3) How many people have 4 pets?

4) How many people have 2 or less than 2 pets?

5) How many people have more than 7 pets?

Scatter Plots

✎ Construct a scatter plot.

x	1	2.5	3	3.5	4	5
y	4	3.5	4.5	2.5	8	2

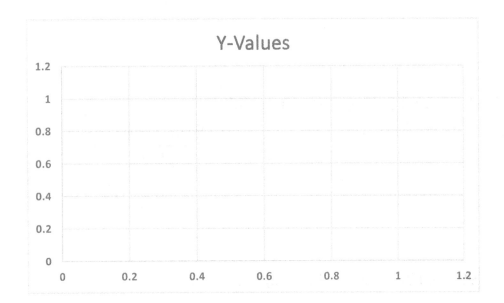

Stem–And–Leaf Plot

✏️ Make stem ad leaf plots for the given data.

1) $42, 14, 17, 21, 44, 24, 18, 47, 23, 24, 19, 12$

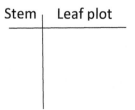

2) $10, 65, 14, 18, 69, 11, 33, 61, 66, 38, 15, 35$

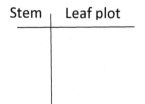

3) $122, 87, 99, 86, 100, 126, 92, 129, 88, 121, 91, 107$

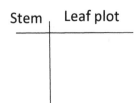

4) $60, 51, 119, 69, 72, 59, 110, 65, 77, 59, 65, 112, 71$

Stem | Leaf plot

The Pie Graph or Circle Graph

Favorite Sports:

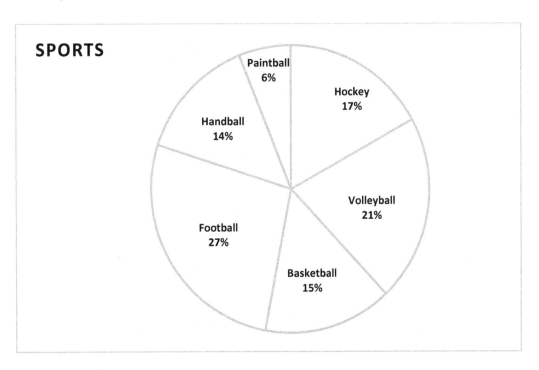

1) What percentage of pie graph is paintball?

2) What percentage of pie graph is Hockey and volleyball?

3) What percentage of pie not Football and Basketball

4) What percentage of pie graph is Hockey and Handball and Football?

5) What percentage of pie graph is Basketball?

6) What percentage of pie not Handball and Paintball?

Probability of Simple Events

✎ Solve.

1) A number is chosen at random from 28 to 35. Find the probability of selecting factors of 5.

2) A number is chosen at random from 1 to 60. Find the probability of selecting multiples of 15.

3) Find the probability of selecting 4queens from a deck of card.

4) A number is chosen at random from 8 to 19. Find the probability of selecting factors of 3.

5) What probability of selecting a ball less than 6 from 10 different bingo balls?

6) A number is chosen at random from 1 to 10. What is the probability of selecting a multiple of 2?

7) A card is chosen from a well-shuffled deck of 52 cards. What is the probability that the card will be a king OR a queen?

8) A number is chosen at random from 1 to 20. What is the probability of selecting multiples of 5.

Answers of Worksheets – Chapter 9

Mean and Median

1) Mean: 8, Median: 8

2) Mean: 8.33, Median: 6.5

3) Mean: 7.85, Median: 8

4) Mean: 5, Median: 3.5

5) Mean: 6.14, Median: 7

6) Mean: 7.57, Median: 9

7) Mean: 8.5, Median: 7.5

8) Mean: 8.14, Median: 6

9) Mean: 29.28, Median: 22

10) Mean: 8.87, Median: 8.5

11) Mean: 31, Median: 28

12) Mean: 48.5, Median: 46

13) Mean: 39.106, Median: 45

14) Mean: 4.8, Median: 4

Mode and Range

1) Mode: 8, Range: 11

2) Mode: 13, Range: 17

3) Mode: 7, Range: 6

4) Mode: 12, Range: 6

5) Mode: 2, Range: 8

6) Mode: 1, Range: 19

7) Mode: 7, Range: 30

8) Mode: 6, Range: 11

9) Mode: 4, Range: 8

10) Mode: 5,10, Range: 8

11) Mode: 12, Range: 16

12) Mode: 3, Range: 13

13) Mode: 22, Range: 32

14) Mode: 13, Range: 11

Times Series

Day	Distance (km)
1	343
2	430
3	268
4	507
5	390

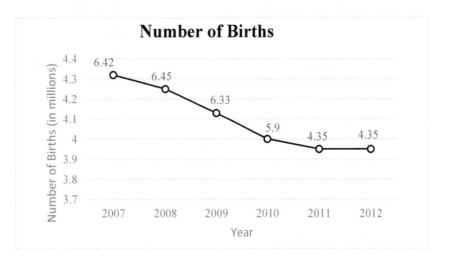

Box and Whisker Plots

1,3, 5, 8, 10, 11, 13, 14, 15, 17,18, 20, 23

Maximum: 23, Minimum: 2, Q_1: 8, Q_2: 13, Q_3: 17

Bar Graph

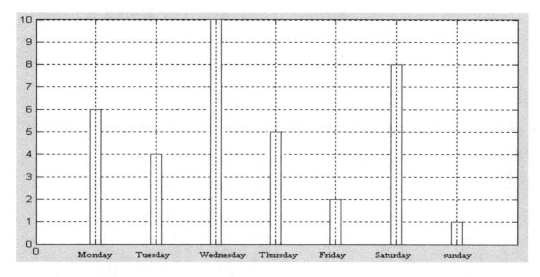

Dot plots

1) 4   3) 4   5) 1

2) 8   4) 6

Scatter Plots

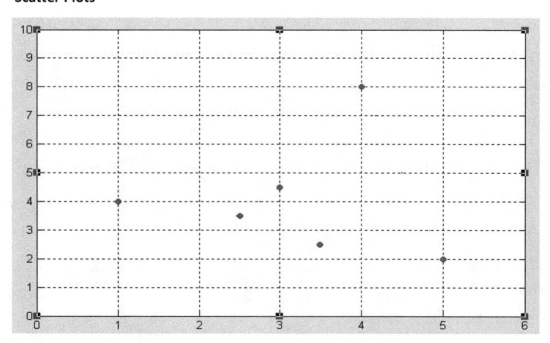

Stem–And–Leaf Plot

1)

Stem	leaf
1	2 4 7 8 9
2	1 3 4
4	2 4 7

2)

Stem	leaf
1	0 1 4 5 8
3	3 5 8
6	1 5 6 9

3)

Stem	leaf
8	6 7 8
9	1 2 9
10	0 7
12	1 2 6 9

4)

Stem	leaf
5	1 9 9
6	0 5 5 9
7	1 2 7
11	0 2 9

The Pie Graph or Circle Graph

1) 6%   3) 58%   5) 15%

2) 38%   4) 58%   6) 80%

Probability of simple events

1) $\frac{1}{4}$ 4) $\frac{1}{3}$ 7) $\frac{2}{13}$

2) $\frac{1}{15}$ 5) $\frac{1}{2}$ 8) $\frac{1}{5}$

3) $\frac{1}{13}$ 6) $\frac{1}{2}$ 9) $\frac{1}{13}$

HiSET Test Review

The High School Equivalency Test (HiSET), commonly known as HiSET, is a standardized test and was released in the year 2014. This test was created by the ITP (Iowa Testing Programs) and ETS (Educational Testing Service). The HiSET is equal to the GED test. Currently, there are twelve states that offer the HiSET®: California, Iowa, Louisiana, Maine, Massachusetts, Missouri, Montana, Nevada, New Hampshire, New Jersey, Tennessee, and Wyoming.

HiSET test takers can choose to take the test using a computer, or with pencil and paper.

The HiSET is made up of five distinct sections:

- o Social Studies,
- o Language Arts Reading
- o Language Arts Writing
- o Science
- o Mathematics

The HiSET Mathematics test is a 90-minute, single-section test that covers basic mathematics topics, quantitative problem-solving and algebraic questions. There are approximately 50 Multiple-choice questions on Mathematics section. Calculator is allowed in the Math section.

In this section, there are two complete HiSET Mathematics Tests. Take these tests to see what score you'll be able to receive on a real HiSET test.

Time to Test

Time to refine your skill with a practice examination

Take a REAL HiSET Mathematics test to simulate the test day experience. After you've finished, score your test using the answer key.

Before You Start

- You'll need a pencil, calculator, and a timer to take the test.
- It's okay to guess. You won't lose any points if you're wrong.
- After you've finished the test, review the answer key to see where you went wrong.

Calculators are permitted for the HiSET Mathematics Test.

Good Luck!

HiSET Mathematics Practice Tests Answer Sheet

Remove (photocopy) this answer sheet and use it to complete the practice test.

HiSET Mathematics Practice Test Answer Sheet

1	Ⓐ Ⓑ Ⓒ Ⓓ Ⓔ	21	Ⓐ Ⓑ Ⓒ Ⓓ Ⓔ	41	Ⓐ Ⓑ Ⓒ Ⓓ Ⓔ
2	Ⓐ Ⓑ Ⓒ Ⓓ Ⓔ	22	Ⓐ Ⓑ Ⓒ Ⓓ Ⓔ	42	Ⓐ Ⓑ Ⓒ Ⓓ Ⓔ
3	Ⓐ Ⓑ Ⓒ Ⓓ Ⓔ	23	Ⓐ Ⓑ Ⓒ Ⓓ Ⓔ	43	Ⓐ Ⓑ Ⓒ Ⓓ Ⓔ
4	Ⓐ Ⓑ Ⓒ Ⓓ Ⓔ	24	Ⓐ Ⓑ Ⓒ Ⓓ Ⓔ	44	Ⓐ Ⓑ Ⓒ Ⓓ Ⓔ
5	Ⓐ Ⓑ Ⓒ Ⓓ Ⓔ	25	Ⓐ Ⓑ Ⓒ Ⓓ Ⓔ	45	Ⓐ Ⓑ Ⓒ Ⓓ Ⓔ
6	Ⓐ Ⓑ Ⓒ Ⓓ Ⓔ	26	Ⓐ Ⓑ Ⓒ Ⓓ Ⓔ	46	Ⓐ Ⓑ Ⓒ Ⓓ Ⓔ
7	Ⓐ Ⓑ Ⓒ Ⓓ Ⓔ	27	Ⓐ Ⓑ Ⓒ Ⓓ Ⓔ	47	Ⓐ Ⓑ Ⓒ Ⓓ Ⓔ
8	Ⓐ Ⓑ Ⓒ Ⓓ Ⓔ	28	Ⓐ Ⓑ Ⓒ Ⓓ Ⓔ	48	Ⓐ Ⓑ Ⓒ Ⓓ Ⓔ
9	Ⓐ Ⓑ Ⓒ Ⓓ Ⓔ	29	Ⓐ Ⓑ Ⓒ Ⓓ Ⓔ	49	Ⓐ Ⓑ Ⓒ Ⓓ Ⓔ
10	Ⓐ Ⓑ Ⓒ Ⓓ Ⓔ	30	Ⓐ Ⓑ Ⓒ Ⓓ Ⓔ	50	Ⓐ Ⓑ Ⓒ Ⓓ Ⓔ
11	Ⓐ Ⓑ Ⓒ Ⓓ Ⓔ	31	Ⓐ Ⓑ Ⓒ Ⓓ Ⓔ		
12	Ⓐ Ⓑ Ⓒ Ⓓ Ⓔ	32	Ⓐ Ⓑ Ⓒ Ⓓ Ⓔ		
13	Ⓐ Ⓑ Ⓒ Ⓓ Ⓔ	33	Ⓐ Ⓑ Ⓒ Ⓓ Ⓔ		
14	Ⓐ Ⓑ Ⓒ Ⓓ Ⓔ	34	Ⓐ Ⓑ Ⓒ Ⓓ Ⓔ		
15	Ⓐ Ⓑ Ⓒ Ⓓ Ⓔ	35	Ⓐ Ⓑ Ⓒ Ⓓ Ⓔ		
16	Ⓐ Ⓑ Ⓒ Ⓓ Ⓔ	36	Ⓐ Ⓑ Ⓒ Ⓓ Ⓔ		
17	Ⓐ Ⓑ Ⓒ Ⓓ Ⓔ	37	Ⓐ Ⓑ Ⓒ Ⓓ Ⓔ		
18	Ⓐ Ⓑ Ⓒ Ⓓ Ⓔ	38	Ⓐ Ⓑ Ⓒ Ⓓ Ⓔ		
19	Ⓐ Ⓑ Ⓒ Ⓓ Ⓔ	39	Ⓐ Ⓑ Ⓒ Ⓓ Ⓔ		
20	Ⓐ Ⓑ Ⓒ Ⓓ Ⓔ	40	Ⓐ Ⓑ Ⓒ Ⓓ Ⓔ		

Practice Test 1

HiSET Mathematics

✓ **50 Questions**

✓ **Total time for this section: 90 Minutes**

✓ **You may use a calculator for this test.**

Administered *Month Year*

1) Two fifth of 45 is equal to $\frac{3}{7}$ of what number?

   A. 25   C. 48   E. 52

   B. 38   D. 42

2) A bag contains 18 balls: seven green, two black, three blue, five red and one white. If 17 balls are removed from the bag at random, what is the probability that a white ball has been removed?

   A. $\frac{1}{17}$ C. $\frac{1}{18}$ E. $\frac{8}{9}$

   B. $\frac{16}{17}$ D. $\frac{17}{18}$

3) What is the value of 6^5?

   A. 776   C. 1,296   E. 7,767

   B. 7,776   D. 6,777

4) What is the median of these numbers? 24, 4, 35, 48, 19, 19, 10, 28, 41

   A. 4   C. 19   E. 24

   B. 10   D. 41

5) The marked price of a computer is E Euro. Its price decreased by 25% in March and later increased by 8 % in April. What is the final price of the computer in E Euro?

   A. 0.79 E   C. 0.081 E   E. 1.06 E

   B. 0.018E   D. 0.81 E

6) 46 is What percent of 40?

   A. 115 %   C. 36 %   E. 15%

   B. 94 %   D. 136 %

7) A rope weighs 350 grams per meter of length. What is the weight in kilograms

of 12.4 meters of this rope? (1 kilograms = 1000 grams)

   A. 0.43   C. 4.34   E. 40.30

   B. 0.4030   D. 4.3

8) What is the value of x in the following figure?

   A. 65

   B. 150

   C. 115

   D. 125

   E. 55

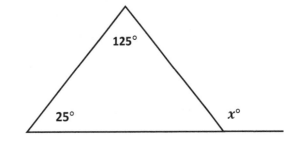

9) Which of the following could be the product of two consecutive prime

numbers? (Select one or more answer choices)

   A. 122   C. 169   E. B, D

   B. 143   D. 77

10) A $50 shirt now selling for $15 is discounted by what percent?

   A. 65 %   C. 54 %   E. 11%

   B. 21 %   D. 70 %

11) The score of Zoe was one fourth of Emma and the score of Harper was twice that of Emma. If the score of Harper was 96, what is the score of Zoe?

    A. 12   C. 24   E. 6

    B. 24   D. 48

12) How many tiles of 2 cm² is needed to cover a floor of dimension 4 cm by 14 cm?

    A. 28   C. 120   E. 20

    B. 24.5   D. 56

13) $(x - 2y)(3x - y) = ?$

    A. $3x^2 - 5xy + 2y^2$ D. $3x^2 - 7xy + y^2$

    B. $2x^2 - 5xy + y^2$ E. $-5x^3 - 4y^3$

    C. $3x^2 - 7xy + 2y^2$

14) Ryan traveled 280 km in 8 hours and Riley traveled 252 km in 6 hours. What is the ratio of the average speed of Ryan to average speed of Riley?

    A. $7:5$ C. $6:5$ E. $5:6$

    B. $5:7$ D. $7:6$

15) An angle is equal to one fifth of its supplement. What is the measure of that angle?

    A. 30   C. 24   E. 12

    B. 16.4   D. 15

16) Abigail purchased a sofa for $386.88. The sofa is regularly priced at $624.

What was the percent discount Abigail received on the sofa?

A. 15 %   C. 62%   E. 12 %

B. 25%   D. 38 %

17) Find the average of the following numbers: 21, 16, 24 and 12?

A. 20.5   C. 73   E. 18

B. 18.25   D. 16

18) When a number is subtracted from 45 and the difference is divided by that

number, the result is 4. What is the value of the number?

A. 12   C. 8   E. 9

B. 15   D. 4

19) Right triangle ABC has two legs of lengths 8 cm (AB) and 6 cm (AC). What

is the length of the third side (BC)?

A. 3 cm   C. 24 cm   E. 10 cm

B. 8 cm   D. 16 cm

20) If the area of trapezoid is 270 cm^2, what is the perimeter of the trapezoid?

A. 100

B. 75

C. 58

D. 38

E. 70

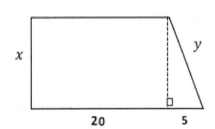

21) A taxi driver earns $16 per hour work. If he works 12 hours a day, and he uses

   3-liters Petrol in 2 hours with price $2.50 for 1-liter. How much money does he

   earn in one day?

    A. $147   C. $145   E. $45

    B. $168   D. $65

22) Solve for x:

$$7(x - 2) + 42 = 3(x + 4)$$

    A. 2   C. 8   E. 4

    B. −8   D. −4

23) The width of a box is one fourth of its length. The height of the box is one half

   of its width. If the length of the box is 48 cm, what is the volume of the box?

    A. 256 cm^3 C. 512 cm^3 E. 2,048 cm^3

    B. 625 cm^3 D. 3,456 cm^3

24) The price of a sofa is decreased by 25% to $465. What was its original price?

    A. $300   C. $620   E. $360

    B. $1,820   D. $610

25) If 40 % of a class are girls, and 35 % of girls play tennis, what percent of the

   class play tennis?

    A. 24 %   C. 60%   E. 20 %

    B. 26 %   D. 14 %

26) The price of a car was $20,000 in 2014, $16,000 in 2015 and $12,800 in 2016.

What is the rate of depreciation of the price of car per year?

A. 25 %   C. 20 %   E. 40%

B. 30 %   D. 35 %

27) Which of the following expressions is equivalent to $5xy(x - y)$?

A. $5yx - 5xy$ D. $-5xy^2 + 5x^2y$

B. $5yx^2 - 5xy$ E. $-5xy^2 - 5yx^2$

C. $5x^2 - 5y^2$

28) The average of three consecutive numbers is 43. What is the smallest number?

A. 45   C. 44   E. 42

B. 43   D. 46

29) The area of a circle is less than 64 π. Which of the following can be the

circumference of the circle? (Select one or more answer choices)

A. 24 π C. 21 π E. 16 π

B. 49 π D. 12 π

30) In four successive hours, a car travels 40 km, 46 km, 43 km, and 45km. In the

next four hours, it travels with an average speed of 45 km per hour. Find the

total distance the car traveled in 8 hours.

A. 354 km   C. 160 km   E. 625 km

B. 356 km   D. 176 km

31) A bank is offering 2.25% simple interest on a savings account. If you deposit $8,000, how much interest will you earn in four years?

   A. $100   C. $720   E. $5,200

   B. $135   D. $1,250

32) If $y = 2c^2 - 3cd + d^2$, what is y when $c = -2$, and $d = 4$?

   A. 16   C. 36   E. 52

   B. 25   D. 125

33) The ratio of boys to girls in a school is 4:3. If there are 420 students in a school, how many boys are in the school.

   A. 145   C. 230   E. 60

   B. 123   D. 240

34) In the xy-plane, the point $(2, -2)$ and $(3, 2)$ are on the line A. Which of the following points could also be on the line A? (Select one or more answer choices)

   A. $(0, 5)$ C. $(-1, 0)$ E. $(2, 5)$

   B. $(1, 3)$ D. $(-1, -14)$

35) In 1999, the average worker's income increased $1,800 per year starting from $24,500 annual salary. Which equation represents income greater than average? (I = income, x = number of years after 1999)

   A. $I > 1,800\,x + 24,500$ D. $I < 24,500\,x + 1800$

   B. $I > 1,800\,x - 24,500$ E. $I < -24,500\,x + 1800$

   C. $I > -1,800\,x + 24,500$

36) If $f(x) = x^2 - 2$, What is the average rate of change of the function

from $x = 3$ to $x = 5$?

A. 9

C. −8

E. 15

B. −9

D. 8

37) The average high of 15 constructions in a town is 140 m, and the average high

of 5 towers in the same town is 160 m. What is the average high of all the 20

structures in that town?

A. 64

C. 145

E. 142

B. 84

D. 140

38) A chemical solution contains 8% alcohol. If there is 19.2 ml of alcohol, what

is the volume of the solution?

A. 520 ml

C. 320 ml

E. 240 ml

B. 144 ml

D. 460 ml

39) The price of a laptop is decreased by 35% to $325. What is its original price?

A. 450

C. 63.75

E. 361.25

B. 488.75

D. 500

40) If 85 % of F is 17 % of M, then F is what percent of M?

A. 5 %

C. 0.05%

E. 500 %

B. 40 %

D. 50 %

41) What are the zeros of the function: $f(x) = 2x^3 - 6x^2 - 8x$?

    A. $0, 1$ C. $0, 1, 4$ E. $0, 1, -4$

    B. $-1, 4$ D. $0, -1, 4$

42) A boat sails 160 miles south and then 120 miles east. How far is the boat from its start point?

    A. 70 miles   C. 20 miles   E. 200 miles

    B. 120 miles   D. 80 miles

43) How many possible outfit combinations come from nine shirts, seven slacks, and 5 times?

    A. 25   C. 25!   E. 315!

    B. 315   D. 80

44) The surface area of a cylinder is $36\pi \ cm^2$. If its height is 7 cm, what is the radius of the cylinder?

    A. 8 cm   C. 12 cm   E. 4 cm

    B. 9 cm   D. 2 cm

45) A shirt costing $500 is discounted 20%. After a month, the shirt is discounted another 10%. Which of the following expressions can be used to find the selling price of the shirt?

    A. $(500) - 500(0.30)$ D. $(500)(0.20) - (240)(0.10)$

    B. $(500)(0.20)(0.10)$ E. $(500)(0.20) - (500)(0.10)$

    C. $(500)(0.80)(0.90)$

46) How long does a 351–miles trip take moving at 45 miles per hour(mph)?

    A. 7 hours and 48 minutes   D. 7 hours

    B. 8 hours and 48 minutes   E. 8 hours

    C. 7 hours and 24 minutes

47) Which of the following lists shows the fractions in order from least to greatest?

    A. $\dfrac{1}{3}, \dfrac{8}{21}, \dfrac{3}{7}$ C. $\dfrac{8}{21}, \dfrac{1}{3}, \dfrac{3}{7}$ E. $\dfrac{1}{3}, \dfrac{3}{7}, \dfrac{8}{21}$

    B. $\dfrac{3}{7}, \dfrac{8}{21}, \dfrac{1}{3}$ D. $\dfrac{3}{7}, \dfrac{1}{3}, \dfrac{8}{21}$

48) Multiply and write the product in scientific notation:

$$(2.6 \times 10^6) \times (4.5 \times 10^{-7})$$

    A. 117×10^2 D. 1170

    B. 1.17×10^{-1} E. 1.17

    C. 11.7×10^{-42}

49) What is the value of y in the following system of equation?

$$4x + 6y = -4$$

$$5x - y = 12$$

    A. -1 D. 4

    B. -2 E. 5

    C. -3

50) If the height of a right pyramid is triple of its side, and its base is a square with side 5 cm. What is its volume?

A. 35 cm^3

B. 75 cm^3

C. 125 cm^3

D. 150 cm^3

E. 250 cm^3

Practice Test 2

HiSET Mathematics

✓ **50 Questions**

✓ **Total time for this section: 90 Minutes**

✓ **You may use a calculator for this test.**

Administered *Month Year*

1) The mean of 70 test scores was calculated as 86. But it turned out that one of the scores was misread as 87 but it was 52. What is the correct mean of the test scores?

A. 86   C. 85.5   E. 84.5

B. 84   D. 85

2) Which of the following graphs represents the compound inequality $-2 \le 3x - 5 < 1$?

A.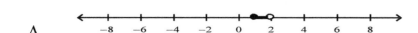

B.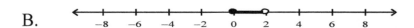

C.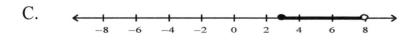

D.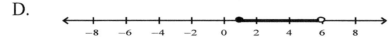

E.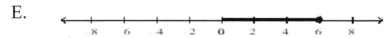

3) Two dice are thrown simultaneously, what is the probability of getting a sum of 5 or 7?

A. $\dfrac{1}{12}$ C. $\dfrac{12}{18}$ E. $\dfrac{2}{18}$

B. $\dfrac{7}{18}$ D. $\dfrac{5}{18}$

4) Simplify the expression.

$$(4x^3 - 9x^2 - 2x^4) - (6x^2 - 5x^4 - 2x^3)$$

A. $-3(x^4 + 2x^3 - 5x^2)$ D. $3(x^4 + 2x^3 - 5x^2)$

B. $2(x^4 + 2x^3 - 5x^2)$ E. $(-3x^4 - 6x^3 - 5x^2)$

C. $3(x^4 + x^3 - 4x^2)$

5) What is the perimeter of a square in centimeters that has an area of 691.69 cm²?

   A. 24.4   C. 74.4   E. 148.8

   B. 105.2   D. 59.5

6) If 75% of A is 25% of B, then B is what percent of A?

   A. 30%   C. 0.03%   E. 300%

   B. 70%   D. 3%

7) If $f(x)=x^4+8x^2-5x-2$ and $g(x)=-1$, what is the value of $(f \circ g)(x) =$?

   A. -11 C. -10 E. 12

   B. 15   D. 14

8) Mr. Matthews saves $4,200 out of his annually family income of $71,400. What fractional part of his income does he save?

   A. $\frac{1}{17}$ C. $\frac{15}{17}$ E. 17

   B. $\frac{12}{17}$ D. $\frac{16}{17}$

9) What is the median of these numbers? 26, 10, 5, 35, 29, 18, 52

   A. 52   C. 35   E. 18

   B. 22.5   D. 26

10) A bank is offering 2.05% simple interest on a savings account. If you deposit $14,000, how much interest will you earn in five years?

   A. $820   C. $3,280   E. $16,400

   B. $1,435   D. $124

11) What are the zeros of the function: $f(x) = 4x^2 + 8x - 96$?

    A. $-24, 2$ C. $0, -48$ E. $12, -8$

    B. $6, -4$ D. $4, -6$

12) Last week 14,000 fans attended a football match. This week four times as many bought tickets, but one seventh of them cancelled their tickets. How many are attending this week?

    A. 72,000   C. 12,000   E. 36,750

    B. 60,000   D. 48,000

13) In two successive years, the population of a town is increased by 5% and 15%. What percent of the population is increased after two years?

    A. 16.2%   C. 9.2 %   E. 20 %

    B. 20.8%   D. 120%

14) Which of the following shows the numbers in descending order?

$$\frac{1}{20}, 0.08, 9\%, \frac{1}{6}$$

    A. $9\%, 0.07, \frac{1}{6}, \frac{1}{20}$ D. $\frac{1}{20}, 0.07, 9\%, \frac{1}{6}$

    B. $9\%, 0.07, \frac{1}{20}, \frac{1}{6}$ E. $\frac{1}{6}, 9\%, 0.07, \frac{1}{20}$

    C. $\frac{1}{6}, \frac{1}{20}, 9\%, 0.07$

15) What is the volume of a box with the following dimensions?

    Height = 4 cm   Width = 9 cm   Length = 5 cm

    A. 180 cm^3 C. 32 cm^3 E. 16 cm^3

    B. 49 cm^3 D. 35 cm^3

16) What is the area of a square whose diagonal is 8?

    A. 8   C. 32   E. 24

    B. 16   D. 28

17) The average of 8 numbers is 32. The average of 5 of those numbers is 50. What is the average of the other three numbers?

    A. 250   C. 2   E. 12

    B. 37   D. 6

18) What is the value of y in the following system of equations?

$$2x + y = -5$$
$$3x - 2y = 10$$

    A. 4   C. 5   E. 0

    B. −4   D. −5

19) If a tree casts a 36–inches shadow while a 9-inches yardstick casts a 6–inches shadow, what is the height of the tree?

    A. 28 in

    B. 144 in

    C. 54 in

    D. $\frac{54}{7}$ in

    E. 8 in

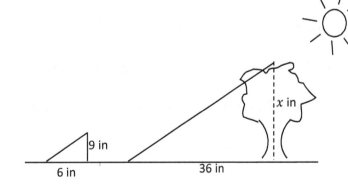

20) The perimeter of a rectangular yard is 72 meters. What is its length if its width is triple its length?

A. 9 meters   C. 27 meters   E. 48 meters

B. 27 meters   D. 19 meters

21) In a stadium the ratio of home fans to visiting fans in a crowd is 8:4. Which of the following could be the total number of fans in the stadium? (Select one or more answer choices)

A. 43,600   C. 51,100   E. 62,500

B. 39,300   D. 50,600

22) What is the equivalent temperature of $104°F$ in Celsius? $C = \frac{5}{9}(F - 32)$

A. 42   C. 40   E. 54

B. 32   D. 80.5

23) Which of the following points lies on the line $5x - 3y = 1$? (Select one or more answer choices)

A. $(5, -6)$ C. $(-1, -2)$ E. $(3, 1)$

B. $(0, -2)$ D. $(2, 4)$

24) Mr. Jefferson family are choosing a menu for their reception. They have 3 choices of appetizers, 9 choices of entrees, 5 choices of cake. How many different menu combinations are possible for them to choose?

A. 15   C. 45   E. 135

B. 35   D. 125

25) Which of the following is equal to the expression below? $(x + y)^2$

A. $2x^2 - 2y^2$

B. $2x^2 + 2y^2$

C. $x^2 + 2xy + y^2$

D. $x^2 - 2xy + y^2$

E. $x^2 + xy + y^2$

26) Anita's trick–or–treat bag contains 21 pieces of chocolate, 16 suckers, 13 pieces of gum, 15 pieces of licorice. If she randomly pulls a piece of candy from her bag, what is the probability of her pulling out a piece of gum?

A. $\dfrac{1}{52}$

B. $\dfrac{1}{13}$

C. $\dfrac{1}{65}$

D. $\dfrac{1}{5}$

E. $\dfrac{13}{52}$

27) The average of four numbers is 46. If a fifth number that is greater than 51 is added, then, which of the following could be the new average? (Select one or more answer choices)

A. 49

B. 46

C. 39

D. 43

E. 45

28) The perimeter of the trapezoid below is 32 cm. What is its area?

A. 70 cm²

B. 60 cm²

C. 140 cm²

D. 124 cm²

E. 132 cm²

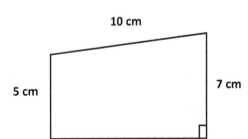

29) A card is drawn at random from a standard 52–card deck, what is the probability that the card is of spades? (The deck includes 13 of each suit clubs, diamonds, hearts, and spades).

A. $\dfrac{4}{52}$ C. $\dfrac{4}{13}$ E. $\dfrac{1}{13}$

B. $\dfrac{1}{4}$ D. $\dfrac{1}{52}$

30) What is the value of the expression $-2(5x + y) + (1 - 5x)^2$ when $x = 1.2$ and $y = -7$?

A. 94   C. 30   E. 27

B. -25 D. -9

31) The ratio of boys and girls in a class is 3:7. If there are 50 students in the class, how many more boys should be enrolled to make the ratio 1:1?

A. 20   C. 35   E. 10

B. 15   D. 4

32) What is the surface area of the cylinder below?

A. $112\ \pi\ in^2$

B. $321\ \pi\ in^2$

C. $213\ \pi\ in^2$

D. $312\ \pi\ in^2$

E. $323\ \pi\ in^2$

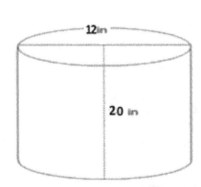

33) Simplify $4x^3y^4(-2xy^2)^4$.

A. $6x^8y^{10}$

B. $-6x^7y^{12}$

C. $64x^7y^{12}$

D. $-64x^8y^{10}$

E. $24x^7y^{12}$

34) Daniel is 20 miles ahead of Noa and running at 4.5 miles per hour. Noa is running at the speed of 7 miles per hour. How long does it take Noa to catch Daniel?

A. 1 hour, and 40 minutes

B. 2 hour, and 30 minutes

C. 8 hours, 20 minutes

D. 8 hours

E. 9 hours

35) A football team had $35,000 to spend on supplies. The team spent $19,000 on new balls. New sport shoes cost $135 each. Which of the following inequalities represent the number of new shoes the team can purchase?

A. $135x + 19,000 \leq 35,000$

B. $135x + 16,000 \leq 35,000$

C. $135x + 35,000 \geq 19,000$

D. $16,000 + 135x \geq 35,000$

E. $19,000 + 135x \geq 35,000$

36) 70 students took an exam and 21 of them failed. What percent of the students passed the exam?

A. 80 %

B. 7 %

C. 3%

D. 70 %

E. 30 %

37) The length of a rectangle is 4 meters less than 7 times its width. The perimeter of the rectangle is 48 meters. What is the area of the rectangle in meters?

A. 336   C. 96   E. 36

B. 192   D. 24

38) If 60 % of a number is 21, what is the number?

A. 6   C. 21   E. 35

B. 15   D. 9

39) The square of a number is $\frac{147}{192}$. What is the cube of that number?

A. $\frac{54}{74}$ C. $\frac{16}{32}$ E. $\frac{1,120}{3,125}$

B. $\frac{343}{512}$ D. $\frac{324}{441}$

40) The circle graph below shows all Mr. Wilson's expenses for last month. If he spent $630 on his car, how much did he spend for his rent?

A. $840

B. $235.20

C. $1,400

D. $4,000

E. $1,210

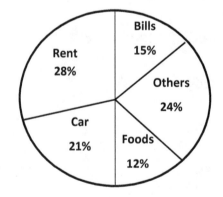

Mr. Wilson's monthly expenses

41) There are three equal tanks of water. If $\frac{3}{8}$ of a tank contains 180 liters of water, what is the capacity of the three tanks of water together?

    A. 2,400 L   C. 1,440 L   E. 600 L

    B. 56.25 L   D. 164.75 L

42) What is the positive value of x in the following equation?

$$|-4x + 3| = 35$$

    A. 9.5   C. 8.25   E. 6

    B. 8   D. 9

43) If 130 % of a number is 104, then what is the 80 % of that number?

    A. 44   C. 64   E. 63

    B. 73   D. 163.8

44) A swimming pool holds 3,600 cubic feet of water. The swimming pool is 24 feet long and 15 feet wide. How deep is the swimming pool?

    A. 1.6   C. 6.6   E. 120

    B. 10   D. 75

45) What is the value of x in the following equation?

$$\frac{5}{9}x + \frac{1}{6} = \frac{1}{2}$$

    A. 5   C. 8   E. $\frac{5}{3}$

    B. $\frac{3}{8}$ D. $\frac{3}{5}$

46) Mrs. Thomson needs an 76% average in her writing class to pass. On her first 3 exams, he earned scores of 68%, 74%, and 88%. What is the minimum score Mrs. Thomson can earn on her fourth and final test to pass?

A. 74   C. 75.5   E. 76.5

B. 86   D. 82

47) Right triangle ABC has two legs of lengths 12 cm (AB) and 16 cm (AC). What is the length of the third side (BC)?

A. 4 cm   C. 6 cm   E. 20 cm

B. 14 cm   D. 8 cm

48) What is the slope of a line that is perpendicular to the line $x - 4y = 8$?

A. 1   C. -1 E. $\frac{1}{4}$

B. 4   D. -4

49) Which set of ordered pairs models a function?

A. $\{(2, 7), (3, 5), (2, 14), (4, 6)\}$

B. $\{(8, 10), (5, 15), (5, 20), (5, 25)\}$

C. $\{(-10, -18), (10, -11), (-10, -13), (10, -14)\}$

D. $\{(1,7), (2, 9), (3, 8), (4, 5)\}$

E. $\{(6, 14), (-7, 20), (6, 20), (-4, 18)$

50) $41 + 9 \times (-14) \div 21 - 13 = ?$

A. 32   C. 28   E. 22

B. 41   D. 19

Answers and Explanations

HiSET Mathematics Practice Tests

Answer Key

✴ Now, it's time to review your results to see where you went wrong and what areas you need to improve!

HiSET Mathematics Practice Tests

Practice Test 1								Practice Test 2							
1	D	16	D	31	C	46	A	1	C	16	C	31	A	46	A
2	D	17	B	32	E	47	A	2	A	17	C	32	D	47	E
3	B	18	E	33	D	48	E	3	D	18	D	33	C	48	B
4	E	19	C	34	D	49	B	4	D	19	C	34	D	49	D
5	D	20	E	35	A	50	C	5	B	20	A	35	A	50	E
6	A	21	A	36	D			6	E	21	B	36	D		
7	C	22	D	37	C			7	E	22	C	37	C		
8	B	23	D	38	E			8	A	23	C	38	E		
9	E	24	C	39	D			9	D	24	E	39	B		
10	D	25	D	40	E			10	B	25	C	40	A		
11	A	26	C	41	D			11	D	26	D	41	C		
12	A	27	D	42	E			12	D	27	A	42	A		
13	C	28	E	43	B			13	B	28	B	43	C		
14	E	29	D	44	D			14	E	29	B	44	B		
15	A	30	A	45	C			15	A	30	E	45	D		

Score Your Test

HiSET scores are reported on a 1–20 score scale in 1-point increments. Each subject test should be passed individually. It means that you must get 8 on each section of the test. If you failed one subject test but did well enough on another to get a total score of 45, that's still not a passing score.

You passed the test if you met the three HiSET passing criteria:

✓ Scored at least 8 out of 20 on each subtest.

✓ Scored at least 2 out of 6 on the essay.

✓ Achieved a total scaled score on all five HiSET subtests of at least 45 out of 100.

here are approximately 50 Multiple-choice questions on Mathematics section. Use the following table to convert HiSET Mathematics raw score to scaled score. (You get 1 point for each correct answer. No points for wrong or skipped answers.)

HiSET Mathematics raw score to scaled score	
Raw Scores	**Scaled Scores**
Below 22 (not passing)	*Below 8*
22 − 30	8 − 10
31 − 36	11 − 13
37 − 44	14 − 16
Above 44	*Above 16*

Practice Test 1

HiSET Mathematics

1) Answer: D

Let x be the number. Write the equation and solve for x.

$\frac{2}{5} \times 45 = \frac{3}{7} \cdot x \Rightarrow \frac{2 \times 45}{5} = \frac{3x}{7}$, use cross multiplication to solve for x.

$14 \times 45 = 3x \times 5 \Rightarrow 630 = 15x \Rightarrow x = 42$

2) Answer: D

If 17 balls are removed from the bag at random, there will be one ball in the bag.

The probability of choosing a white ball is 1 out of 18. Therefore, the probability of not choosing a white ball is 17 out of 18 and the probability of having not a white ball after removing 17 balls is the same.

3) Answer: B

$6^5 = 6 \times 6 \times 6 \times 6 \times 6 = 7,776$

4) Answer: E

Write the numbers in order:

4, 10, 19, 19, 24, 28, 35, 41, 48

Since we have 9 numbers (9 is odd), then the median is the number in the middle, which is 24.

5) Answer: D

To find the discount, multiply the number by (100% – rate of discount).

Therefore, for the first discount we get: $(100\% - 25\%)(E) = (0.75)E$

For increase of 8 %:

$(0.75)E \times (100\% + 8\%) = (0.75)(1.08) = 0.81E$.

6) Answer: A

Use percent formula: $Part = \frac{percent \times whole}{100}$

$46 = \frac{percent \times 40}{100} \Rightarrow \frac{46}{1} = \frac{percent \times 40}{100}$, cross multiply.

$4,600 = percent \times 40$, divide both sides by 40: $115 = percent$

7) Answer: C

The weight of 12.4 meters of this rope is: $12.4 \times 350g = 4,340g$

1 kg = 1,000 g, therefore, $4,340\ g \div 1000 = 4.34kg$

8) Answer: B

$x = 25 + 125 = 150$

9) Answer: E

Some of prime numbers are: 2, 3, 5, 7, 11, 13

Find the product of two consecutive prime numbers:

$5 \times 7 = 35$ (not in the options)

$7 \times 11 = 77$ (not in the options)

$11 \times 13 = 143$ (bingo!)

$13 \times 17 = 221$ (not in the options)

Choice E is correct.

10) Answer: D

Use the formula for Percent of Change: $\dfrac{\text{New Value} - \text{Old Value}}{\text{Old Value}} \times 100\ \%$

$\dfrac{50-15}{50} \times 100\ \% = -70\ \%$ (negative sign here means that the new price is less than old price).

11) Answer: A

If the score of Harper was 96, therefore the score of Emma is 48. Since, the score of Zoe was one fourth of Emma, therefore, the score of Zoe is 12.

12) Answer: A

The area of the floor is: $4\ cm \times 14\ cm = 56\ cm^2$

The number of tiles needed $= 56 \div 2 = 28$

13) Answer: C

Use FOIL (First, Out, In, Last)

$(x - 2y)(3x - y) = 3x^2 - xy - 6xy + 2y^2 = 3x^2 - 7xy + 2y^2$

14) Answer: E

The average speed of Ryan is: $280 \div 8 = 35$ km

The average speed of Riley is: $252 \div 6 = 42$ km

Write the ratio and simplify.

$35: 42 \Rightarrow 5: 6$.

15) Answer: A

The sum of supplement angles is 180. Let x be that angle. Therefore,

$x + 5x = 180$.

$6x = 180$, divide both sides by 6: $x = 30$.

16) Answer: D

Use percent formula:

$Part = \frac{percent \times whole}{100}$

$386.88 = \frac{percent \times 624}{100} \Rightarrow$ (cross multiply): $38,688 = percent \times 624 \Rightarrow$

$percent = \frac{38,688}{624} = 62$

386.88 is 62 % of 624. Therefore, the discount is: $100\% - 62\% = 38\%$.

17) Answer: B

$average = \frac{sum\ of\ terms}{number\ of\ terms} \Rightarrow average = \frac{(21+16+24+12)}{4} \Rightarrow \frac{73}{4} = 18.25$

18) Answer: E

Let x be the number. Write the equation and solve for x.

$\frac{(45-x)}{x} = 4$ (cross multiply)

$(45 - x) = 4x$, then add x both sides. $45 = 5x$, now divide both sides by 5. $\Rightarrow x = 9$.

19) Answer: C

Use Pythagorean Theorem: $a^2 + b^2 = c^2$

$8^2 + 6^2 = C^2 \Rightarrow 64 + 36 = C^2 \Rightarrow 100 = c^2 \Rightarrow c = 10$

20) Answer: E

The area of the trapezoid is: $Area = \frac{1}{2}h(b_1 + b_2) = \frac{1}{2}(x)(25 + 20) = 270$

$\rightarrow 22.5x = 270 \rightarrow x = 12$

$y = \sqrt{5^2 + 12^2} = \sqrt{25 + 144} = \sqrt{169} = 13$

The perimeter of the trapezoid is: $12 + 20 + 13 + 25 = 70$

21) Answer: A

$\$16 \times 12 = \$192$

Petrol use: $3 \div 2 = 1.5, 12 \times 1.5 = 18$ liters

Petrol cost: $18 \times \$2.50 = \$45$

Money earned: $\$192 - \$45 = \$147$

22) Answer: D

Simplify:

$7(x - 2) + 42 = 3(x + 4)$

$7x - 14 + 42 = 3x + 12 \Rightarrow 7x + 28 = 3x + 12$

Subtract $3x$ from both sides:

$4x + 28 = 12$, Subtract 28 to both sides: $4x = -16 \Rightarrow x = -4$

23) Answer: D

If the length of the box is 48, then the width of the box is one fourth of it, 12, and the height of the box is 6 (one half of the width). The volume of the box is:

$V = lwh = (48)(12)(6) = 3,456$

24) Answer: C

Let x be the original price.

If the price of the sofa is decreased by 25% to $465, then: $75 \% \ of \ x = 465 \Rightarrow 0.75x = 465 \Rightarrow x = 465 \div 0.75 = 620$

25) Answer: D

The percent of girls playing tennis is: $40 \% \times 35 \% = 0.40 \times 0.35 = 0.14 = 14 \%$

26) Answer: C

Use this formula: Percent of Change $= \dfrac{New\ Value - Old\ Value}{Old\ Value} \times 100 \%$

$\dfrac{16,000 - 20,000}{20,000} \times 100 \% = -20 \%$ and $\dfrac{12,800 - 16,000}{16,000} \times 100\% = -20 \%$

27) Answer: D

Use distributive property:

$5xy(x - y) = 5xy(x) + 5xy(-y) = 5yx^2 - 5xy^2$

28) Answer: E

Let x be the smallest number. Then, these are the numbers: $x, x + 1, x + 2$

$average = \frac{\text{sum of terms}}{\text{number of terms}} \Rightarrow 43 = \frac{x+(x+1)+(x+2)}{3} \Rightarrow 43 = \frac{3x+3}{3} \Rightarrow 43 = x + 1 \Rightarrow x = 42$

29) Answer: D

Area of the circle is less than $64\,\pi$. Use the formula of areas of circles.

$$Area = \pi r^2 \Rightarrow \pi r^2 < 64\pi \Rightarrow r^2 < 64 \Rightarrow r < 8$$

Radius of the circle is less than 8. Let's put 8 for the radius. Now, use the circumference formula: Circumference $= 2\pi r = 2\pi\,(8) = 16\,\pi$

Since the radius of the circle is less than 8. Then, the circumference of the circle must be less than $16\,\pi$. Choices D is less than $16\,\pi$

30) Answer: A

Add the first 4 numbers. $40 + 46 + 43 + 45 = 174$

To find the distance traveled in the next 4 hours, multiply the average by number of hours.

$Distance = Average \times Rate = 45 \times 4 = 180$

Add both numbers. $174 + 180 = 354$

31) Answer: C

Use simple interest formula: $I = prt$

$(I = interest, p = principal, r = rate, t = time)$

$$I = (8,000)(0.0225)(4) = 720$$

32) Answer: E

$y = 2c^2 - 3cd + d^2$

Plug in the values of a and b in the equation: $c = -2$ and $d = 4$

$y = 2(-2)^2 - 3(-2)(4) + (4)^2 = 8 - 3(-8) + 16 = 36 + 16 = 52$

33) Answer: D

The ratio of boy to girls is 4:3. Therefore, there are 4 boys out of 7 students. To find the answer, first divide the total number of students by 7, then multiply the result by 4.

$420 \div 7 = 60 \Rightarrow 60 \times 4 = 240$

34) Answer: D

The equation of a line is in the form of $y = mx + b$, where m is the slope of the line and b is the $y - intercept$ of the line.

Two points $(2, -2)$ and $(3,2)$ are online A. Therefore, the slope of the line A is:

slope of line A$= \frac{y_2 - y_1}{x_2 - x_1} = \frac{2-(-2)}{3-2} = \frac{4}{1} = 4$

The slope of line A is 4. Thus, the formula of the line A is:

$y = mx + b = 4x + b$, choose a point and plug in the values of x and y in the equation to solve for b. Let's choose point $(3, 2)$. Then:

$$y = 4x + b \rightarrow 2 = 12 + b \rightarrow b = 2 - 12 = -10$$

The equation of line A is: $y = 4x - 10$

Now, let's review the choices provided:

A. $(0, 5)$ $y = 4x - 10 \rightarrow 5 = 0 - 10 = -10$, This is not true.

B. $(1, 3)$ $y = 4x - 10 \rightarrow 3 = 4 - 10 = -6$, This is not true.

C. $(-1,0)$ $y = 4x - 10 \rightarrow 0 = -4 - 10 = -14$ This is not true.

D. $(-1, -14)$ $y = 4x - 10 \rightarrow -14 = -4 - 10 = -14$, This is true!

E. $(2, 5)$ $y = 4x - 10 \rightarrow 5 = 8 - 10 = -2$, This is not true.

35) Answer: A

Let x be the number of years. Therefore, $1,800 per year equals $1,800x$.

starting from $24,500 annual salary means you should add that amount to $1,800x$.

Income more than that is: $I > 1,800x + 24,500$

36) Answer: D

Rate of change$= \frac{y_2 - y_1}{x_2 - x_1}$

$f(x) = x^2 - 2$, from $x = 3$, to $x = 5$, then $f(3) = 3^2 - 2 = 7$, and $f(5) = 5^2 - 2 = 23$. $\frac{23-7}{5-3} = \frac{16}{2} = 8$

37) Answer: C

average $= \frac{\text{sum of terms}}{\text{number of terms}}$

The sum of the high of all constructions is: $15 \times 140 = 2,100$ m

The sum of the high of all towers is: $5 \times 160 = 800$ m

The sum of the high of all building is: $2{,}100 + 800 = 2{,}900$

$average = \dfrac{2{,}900}{20} = 145$

38) Answer: E

8% of the volume of the solution is alcohol. Let x be the volume of the solution. Then:

8% of $x = 19.2$ ml

$0.08\ x = 19.2 \Rightarrow \dfrac{8x}{100} = \dfrac{192}{10}$ cross multiply

$80x = 19{,}200 \Rightarrow$ (devide by 80) $x = 240$

39) Answer: D

Let x be the original price.

If the price of a laptop is decreased by 35% to \$325, then:

$65\ \%\ of\ x = 325 \Rightarrow 0.65x = 325 \Rightarrow x = 325 \div 0.65 = 500$

40) Answer: E

Write the equation and solve for M:

0.85 F = 0.17 M, divide both sides by 0.17, then:

$\dfrac{0.85}{0.17}$ F = M, therefore: M = 5 F, and M is 5 times of F or it's 500% of F.

41) Answer: D

Frist factor the function:

$2x^3 - 6x^2 - 8x = 2x\ (x^2 - 3x - 4) = 2x(x - 4)(x + 1)$

To find the zeros, $f(x)$ should be zero. $f(x) = 2x(x - 4)(x + 1) = 0$

Therefore, the zeros are: $x = 0$

$(x - 4) = 0 \Rightarrow x = 4$

$(x + 1) = 0 \Rightarrow x = -1$

42) Answer: E

Use the information provided in the question to draw the shape.

Use Pythagorean Theorem: $a^2 + b^2 = c^2 \Rightarrow 120^2 + 160^2 = c^2$

$\Rightarrow 14{,}400 + 25{,}600 = c^2 \Rightarrow 40{,}000 = c^2 \Rightarrow c = 200.$

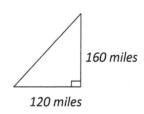

160 miles

120 miles

43) Answer: B

To find the number of possible outfit combinations, multiply number of options for each factor: $9 \times 7 \times 5 = 315$

44) Answer: D

Formula for the Surface area of a cylinder is:

$SA = 2\pi r^2 + 2\pi rh \rightarrow 36\pi = 2\pi r^2 + 2\pi r(7) \rightarrow r^2 + 7r - 18 = 0$

$(r + 9)(r - 2) = 0 \rightarrow r = 2 \quad or \quad r = -9 \ (unacceptable)$

45) Answer: C

To find the discount, multiply the number by (100% – rate of discount).

Therefore, for the first discount we get: $(500)(100\% - 20\%) = (500)(0.8)$

For the next 10 % discount: $(500)(0.80)(0.90)$.

46) Answer: A

Use distance formula:

Distance $=$ Rate $\times$ time $\Rightarrow 351 = 45 \times$ T, divide both sides by 45. $\Rightarrow T = 7.8$ hours.

Change hours to minutes for the decimal part. 0.6 hours $= 0.8 \times 60 = 48 \ minutes$.

47) Answer: A

Let's compare each fraction:

$\frac{1}{3}=0.333, \frac{8}{21}=0.38, \frac{3}{7}=0.428$

$\frac{1}{3} < \frac{8}{21} < \frac{3}{7}$ Only choice A provides the right order.

48) Answer: E

$(2.6 \times 10^6) \times (4.5 \times 10^{-7}) = (2.6 \times 4.5) \times (10^6 \times 10^{-7}) = 11.7 \times (10^{(6-7)}) =$

$11.7 \times 10^{-1} = 1.17$

49) Answer: B

Solving Systems of Equations by Elimination

$4x + 6y = -4$
$5x - y = 12$ Multiply the first equation by 5, and second equation by -4, then add

two equations.

$$\begin{aligned} 5(4x + 6y = -4) \\ -4(5x - y = 12) \end{aligned} \Rightarrow \begin{aligned} 20x + 30y = -20 \\ -20x + 4y = -48 \end{aligned} \Rightarrow 34y = -68 \Rightarrow y = -2.$$

50) Answer: C

The formula of the volume of pyramid is:

$$V = \frac{l \times w \times h}{3}$$

The length and width of the pyramid is 5 cm and its height is 15 cm. Therefore:

$$V = \frac{5 \times 5 \times 15}{3} = 125 \ cm^3$$

Practice Test 2

HiSET Mathematics

1) Answer: C

average (mean) = $\frac{\text{sum of terms}}{\text{number of terms}} \Rightarrow 86 = \frac{\text{sum of terms}}{70} \Rightarrow$ sum $= 86 \times 70 = 6{,}020$

The difference of 87 and 52 is 35. Therefore, 35 should be subtracted from the sum.

$6{,}020 - 35 = 5{,}985$

mean $= \frac{\text{sum of terms}}{\text{number of terms}} \Rightarrow$ mean $= \frac{5{,}985}{70} = 85.5$

2) Answer: A

Solve for x. $-2 \le 3x - 5 < 1$

$\Rightarrow$ (add 5 all sides) $-2 + 5 \le 3x - 5 + 5 < 1 + 5 \Rightarrow 3 \le 3x < 6$

$\Rightarrow$ (divide all sides by 3) $1 \le x < 2$

x is between 1 and 2. Choice A represent this inequality.

3) Answer: D

To get a sum of 5 for two dice, we can get 4 different options:

$(1, 4), (2, 3), (4, 1), (3, 2)$

To get a sum of 7 for two dice, we can get 6 different options:

$(1, 6), (2, 5), (3, 4), (4, 3), (5, 2), (6, 1)$

Therefore, there are 10 options to get the sum of 5 or 7.

Since, we have $6 \times 6 = 36$ total options, the probability of getting a sum of 5 or 7 is 10 out of 36 or $\frac{5}{18}$.

4) Answer: D

Simplify and combine like terms.

$(4x^3 - 9x^2 - 2x^4) - (6x^2 - 5x^4 - 2x^3) \Rightarrow (4x^3 - 9x^2 - 2x^4) - 6x^2 + 5x^4 + 2x^3$

$\Rightarrow 3x^4 + 6x^3 - 15x^2 = 3(x^4 + 2x^3 - 5x^2)$.

5) Answer: B

The area of the square is 691.69. Therefore, the side of the square is square root of the area.

$\sqrt{691.69} = 26.3$

Four times the side of the square is the perimeter: $4 \times 26.3 = 105.2$

6) Answer: E

Write the equation and solve for B: 0.75 A = 0.25 B, divide both sides by 0.25, then:

$\frac{0.75}{0.25}$ A = B, therefore: B = 3 A, and B is 3 times of A or it's 300% of A.

7) Answer: E

$f(x) = x^4 + 8x^2 - 5x - 2$, and $g(x) = -1$, then $(f \circ g)(x) = f(g(x)) = f(-1) =$

$(-1)^4 + 8(-1)^2 - 5(-1) - 2 = 1 + 8 + 5 - 2 = 12$

8) Answer: A

4,200 out of 71,400 equals to $\frac{4,200}{71,400} = \frac{42}{714} = \frac{6}{102} = \frac{1}{17}$

9) Answer: D

Write the numbers in order: 5, 10, 18, 26, 29, 35, 52

Median is the number in the middle. So, the median is 26.

10) Answer: B

Use simple interest formula: $I = prt$ (I = interest, p = principal, r = rate, t = time)

$I = (14,000)(0.0205)(5) = 1,435$

11) Answer: D

To find the zeros, $f(x)$ should be zero.

$f(x) = ax^2 + bx + c = 0 \Rightarrow x = \frac{-b \pm \sqrt{b^2 - 4ac}}{2a}$

$f(x) = 4x^2 + 8x - 96 = 0, \Rightarrow x = \frac{-8 \pm \sqrt{8^2 - 4(4)(-96)}}{2(4)} = \frac{-8 \pm \sqrt{1600}}{8}$

$\Rightarrow x = \begin{cases} \frac{-8+40}{8} = \frac{32}{8} = 4 \\ \frac{-8-40}{8} = \frac{-48}{8} = -6 \end{cases}$

12) Answer: D

Four times of 14,000 is 56,000. One seventh of them cancelled their tickets.

One seventh of 56,000 equal 8,000 ($\frac{1}{7} \times 56,000 = 8,000$).

$(56,000 - 8,000 = 48,000)$ fans are attending this week

13) Answer: B

the population is increased by 5% and 15%. 5% increase changes the population to 115% of original population.

For the second increase, multiply the result by 115%.

$(1.05) \times (1.15) = 1.2075 = 120.8\%$

20.8 percent of the population is increased after two years.

14) Answer: E

Change the numbers to decimal and then compare.

$\frac{1}{6} = 0.1666 \dots$

0.08

$9\% = 0.09$

$\frac{1}{20} = 0.05$

Therefore $\frac{1}{6} > 9\% > 0.08 > \frac{1}{20}$.

15) Answer: A

Volume of a box = length × width × height = $4 \times 9 \times 5 = 180$

16) Answer: C

The diagonal of the square is 8. Let x be the side.

Use Pythagorean Theorem: $a^2 + b^2 = c^2$

$x^2 + x^2 = 8^2 \Rightarrow 2x^2 = 64 \Rightarrow x^2 = 32 \Rightarrow x = \sqrt{32}$

The area of the square is: $\sqrt{32} \times \sqrt{32} = 32$

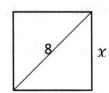

17) Answer: C

average $= \frac{\text{sum of terms}}{\text{number of terms}} \Rightarrow 32 = \frac{\text{sum of 8 numbers}}{8} \Rightarrow$ sum of 8 numbers $= 32 \times 8 = 256$

$50 = \frac{\text{sum of 5 numbers}}{5} \Rightarrow$ sum of 5 numbers $= 5 \times 50 = 250$

sum of 8 numbers – sum of 5 numbers = sum of 3 numbers

$256 - 250 = 6$

average of 3 numbers $= \frac{6}{3} = 2$.

18) Answer: D

Solving Systems of Equations by Elimination

$\begin{array}{l} 2x + y = -5 \\ 3x - 2y = 10 \end{array}$ Multiply the first equation by 3, and second equation by -2, then add two equations.

$\begin{array}{l} 3(2x + y = -5) \\ -2(3x - 2y = 10) \end{array} \Rightarrow \begin{array}{l} 6x + 3y = -15 \\ -6x + 4y = -20 \end{array} \Rightarrow 7y = -35 \Rightarrow y = -5.$

19) Answer: C

Write a proportion and solve for x.

$\frac{6}{9} = \frac{36}{x} \Rightarrow 6x = 9 \times 36 \Rightarrow x = 54$ in

20) Answer: A

The width of the rectangle is triple its length. Let x be the length. Then, $width = 3x$

Perimeter of the rectangle is 2 (width + length) = $2(3x + x) = 72 \Rightarrow 8x = 72 \Rightarrow x = 9$

Length of the rectangle is 9 meters.

21) Answer: B

In the stadium the ratio of home fans to visiting fans in a crowd is 8:4. Therefore, total number of fans must be divisible by 12: 8 + 4 = 12.

Let's review the choices:

    A. 43,600: 43,600 ÷ 12 = 3,633.3

    B. 39,300: 39,300 ÷ 12 = 3,275

    C. 51,100: 51,100 ÷ 12 = 4,258.3

    D. 50,600: 50,600 ÷ 12 = 4,216.6

    E. 62,500: 62,500 ÷ 12 = 5,208.3

    Only choice B when divided by 12 result a whole number.

22) Answer: C

Plug in 104 for F and then solve for C.

$C = \frac{5}{9}(F - 32) \Rightarrow C = \frac{5}{9}(104 - 32) \Rightarrow C = \frac{5}{9}(72) = 40.$

23) Answer: C

$5x - 3y = 1$. Plug in the values of x and y from choices provided. Then:

    A. $(5, -6)$: $5(5) - 3(-6) = -25 + 18 = -7$, This is NOT true!

    B. $(0, -2)$: $5(0) - 3(-2) = 0 + 6 = 6$, This is NOT true!

    C. $(-1, -2)$: $5(-1) - 3(-2) = -5 + 6 = 1$, This is true!

    D. $(2, 4)$: $5(2) - 3(4) = 10 - 12 = -2$, This is NOT true!

    E. $(3, 1)$: $5(3) - 3(1) = 15 - 3 = 12$, This is NOT true!

24) Answer: E

To find the number of possible outfit combinations, multiply number of options for each factor: $3 \times 9 \times 5 = 135$

25) Answer: C

Use FOIL method.

$$(x + y)^2 = (x + y)(x + y) = x^2 + xy + xy + y^2 = x^2 + 2xy + y^2$$

26) Answer: D

$$\text{Probability} = \frac{number\ of\ desired\ outcomes}{number\ of\ total\ outcomes} = \frac{13}{21+16+13+15} = \frac{13}{65} = \frac{1}{5}$$

27) Answer: A

First, find the sum of six numbers.

$$\text{average} = \frac{sum\ of\ terms}{number\ of\ terms} \Rightarrow 46 = \frac{sum\ of\ 4\ numbers}{4} \Rightarrow sum\ of\ 4\ numbers = 4 \times 46 = 184$$

The sum of 4 numbers is 184. If a fifth number that is greater than 51 is added to these numbers, then the sum of 5 numbers must be greater than 235 ($184 + 51 = 235$).

If the number was 51, then the average of the numbers is:

$$\text{average} = \frac{sum\ of\ terms}{number\ of\ terms} = \frac{235}{5} = 47$$

Since the number is bigger than 51. Then, the average of five numbers must be greater than 47. Choices A is greater than 47.

28) Answer: B

The perimeter of the trapezoid is 32 cm.

Therefore, the missing side (height) is $= 32 - 7 - 10 - 5 = 10$

Area of a trapezoid: $A = \frac{1}{2}h(b1 + b2) = \frac{1}{2}(10)(5 + 7) = 60$

29) Answer: B

The probability of choosing a spade is $\frac{13}{52} = \frac{1}{4}$

30) Answer: E

Plug in the value of x and y. $-2(5x + y) + (1 - 5x)^2$ when $x = 1.2$ and $y = -7$

$= -2(5(1.2) + (-7)) + (1 - 5(1.2))^2 = -2(6 - 7) + (1 - 6))^2 = (-2)(-1) + (-5)^2$

$= 2 + 25 = 27$

31) Answer: A

The ratio of boy to girls is 3: 7. Therefore, there are 3 boys out of 10 students. To find the answer, first divide the total number of students by 10, then multiply the result by 3.

$50 \div 10 = 5 \Rightarrow 5 \times 3 = 15$

There are 15 boys and 35 (50 – 15) girls. So, 20 more boys should be enrolled to make the ratio 1:1

32) Answer: D

Surface Area of a cylinder = $2\pi r (r + h)$,

The radius of the cylinder is 6 (12 ÷ 2) inches and its height is 20 inches. Therefore,

Surface Area of a cylinder = $2\pi (6) (6 + 20) = 312\pi$

33) Answer: C

Simplify. $4x^3y^4(-2xy^2)^4 = 4x^3y^4(16x^4y^8) = 64x^7y^{12}$

34) Answer: D

The distance between Daniel and Noa is 20 miles. Daniel running at 4.5 miles per hour and Noa is running at the speed of 7 miles per hour. Therefore, every hour the distance is 2.5 miles less. $20 \div 2.5 = 8$.

35) Answer: A

Let x be the number of new shoes the team can purchase. Therefore, the team can purchase 135 x.

The team had $35,000 and spent $19,000. Now the team can spend on new shoes $16,000 at most. Now, write the inequality: $135x + 19,000 \le 35,000$

36) Answer: D

The failing rate is 21 out of 70, $\frac{21}{70}$

Change the fraction to percent: $\frac{21}{70} \times 100\% = 30\%$

30 percent of students failed. Therefore, 70 percent of students passed the exam.

37) Answer: C

Let L be the length of the rectangular and W be the width of the rectangular. Then,

$L = 7W - 4$

The perimeter of the rectangle is 54 meters. Therefore: $2L + 2W = 48$

$L + W = 24$

Replace the value of L from the first equation into the second equation and solve for W:

$(7W - 4) + W = 24 \rightarrow 8W - 8 = 24 \rightarrow 8W = 32 \rightarrow W = 4$

The width of the rectangle is 7 meters, and its length is:

$L = 7W - 4 = 7(4) - 4 = 24$

The area of the rectangle is: length × width = 24 × 4 = 96

38) Answer: E

Let x be the number. Write the equation and solve for x.

$60\% \ of \ x = 21 \Rightarrow 0.60 \ x = 21 \Rightarrow x = 21 \div 0.60 = 35$

39) Answer: B

$\frac{147}{192}$, simplify by 3, then the number is the square root of $\frac{49}{64}$: $\sqrt{\frac{49}{64}} = \frac{7}{8}$

The cube of the number is: $(\frac{7}{8})^3 = \frac{343}{512}$

40) Answer: A

Let x be all expenses, then $\frac{21}{100}x = \$630 \rightarrow x = \frac{100 \times \$630}{21} = \$3,000$

He spent for his rent: $\frac{28}{100} \times \$3,000 = \$840$

41) Answer: C

Let x be the capacity of one tank. Then, $\frac{3}{8}x = 180 \rightarrow x = \frac{8 \times 180}{3} = 480$ L

The amount of water in three tanks is equal to: 3 × 480 = 1,440 Liters

42) Answer: A

To solve absolute values equations, write two equations.

$-4x + 3$ can equal positive 35, or negative 35. Therefore,

$-4x + 3 = 35 \Rightarrow -4x = 32 \Rightarrow x = -8$

$-4x + 3 = -35 \Rightarrow -4x = -35 - 3 \Rightarrow x = 9.5$

43) Answer: C

First, find the number.

Let x be the number. Write the equation and solve for x.

130 % of a number is 104, then:

$1.3 \times x = 104 \Rightarrow x = 104 \div 1.3 = 80$

80 % of 80 is: $0.8 \times 80 = 64$

44) Answer: B

Use formula of rectangle prism volume.

V = (length) (width) (height) $\Rightarrow 3,600 = (24) (15)$ (height) $\Rightarrow$ height $= 3,600 \div 360 = 10$

45) Answer: D

Isolate and solve for x.

$\frac{5}{9}x + \frac{1}{6} = \frac{1}{2} \Rightarrow \frac{5}{9}x = \frac{1}{2} - \frac{1}{6} = \frac{1}{3} \Rightarrow \frac{5}{9}x = \frac{1}{3}$

Multiply both sides by the reciprocal of the coefficient of x: $(\frac{9}{5})\frac{5}{9}x = \frac{1}{3}(\frac{9}{5}) \Rightarrow x = \frac{9}{15} = \frac{3}{5}$

46) Answer: A

Mrs. Thomson needs an 76% average to pass for four exams. Therefore, the sum of 4

exams must be at lease $4 \times 76 = 304$

The sum of 3 exams is: $68 + 74 + 88 = 230$

The minimum score Mrs. Thomson can earn on her fourth and final test to pass is:

$304 - 230 = 74$

47) Answer: E

Use Pythagorean Theorem: $a^2 + b^2 = c^2$

$12^2 + 16^2 = c^2 \Rightarrow 400 = c^2 \Rightarrow c = 20$

48) Answer: B

The equation of a line in slope intercept form is: $y = mx + b$

Solve for y.

$x - 4y = 8 \rightarrow -4y = -x + 8$

Divide both sides by (-4). Then:

$y = \frac{1}{4}x - 2$

The slope of this line is $\frac{1}{4}$.

The product of the slopes of two perpendicular lines is -1. Therefore, the slope of a line that is perpendicular to this line is:

$m_1 \times m_2 = -1 \Rightarrow \frac{1}{4} \times m_2 = -1 \Rightarrow m_2 = \frac{-1}{\frac{1}{4}} = -4$

49) Answer: D

$(1, 7), (2, 9), (3, 8), (4, 5)$

A function is a relation in which each element in the domain corresponds to exactly one element of the range. Then, option D is function.

50) Answer: E

Use PEMDAS (order of operation):

$41 + 9 \times (-14) \div 21 - 13 = 41 + (-126 \div 21) - 13 = 41 + (-6) - 13 = 22.$

"End"